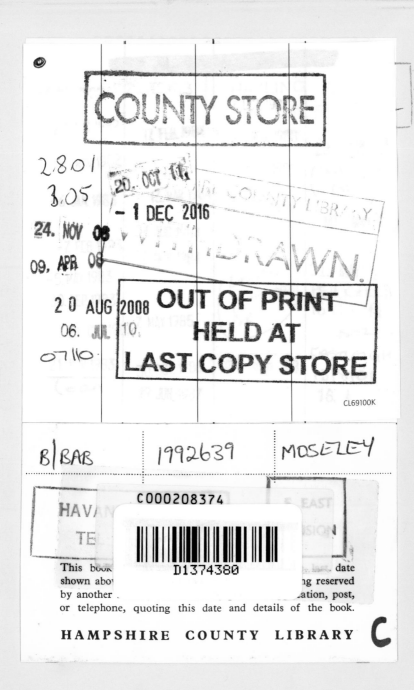

Irascible Genius

A LIFE OF CHARLES BABBAGE, INVENTOR

CHARLES BABBAGE

... Under the dark
　Of Destiny Charles Babbage seemed to stand—
True servant still to science, yet a mark
　For fewer boons than buffets at her hand.

In no scant measure these were dealt to him,
　From far off days, when he was first to range
Lone analytic heights, through pathways dim,
　By lettered sign and symbol quaint and strange.
　　　　　　　　　　Punch　November 4 1871

From 'Burgoyne—Murchison—Babbage', reprinted by permission of *Punch*.

MABOTH MOSELEY

Irascible Genius

A LIFE OF
CHARLES BABBAGE, INVENTOR

*

FOREWORD BY B.V. BOWDEN,
Principal, the Manchester College of Science and Technology

HUTCHINSON OF LONDON

HUTCHINSON & CO. (*Publishers*) LTD
178–202 Great Portland Street, London, W.1

London Melbourne Sydney
Auckland Bombay Toronto
Johannesburg New York

★

First published 1964

For Margaret Hornby

Acknowledgements

*

CHARLES BABBAGE was a prolific writer but he ignored some of the most important details of his private life, and for helping me to close this gap I am deeply indebted to Mr. Richard H. Babbage, great-grandson of Charles Babbage and grandson of Major-General Henry P. Babbage. Other descendants to whom I owe grateful thanks are Mrs. M. A. Phillips, Mr. Gordon S. Babbage and the Rev. S. Barton Babbage, M.A., PH.D.

Similarly I am indebted to the Earl of Lytton for his permission to quote from letters and documents preserved in the collection of Lord Byron's grandson, the second Earl of Lovelace, known as the Lovelace Papers.

To Mr. and Mrs. Malcolm Elwin I owe special thanks for their kind hospitality and for so patiently explaining some aspects of Lady Lovelace's life which perplexed me.

My gratitude to Dr. B. V. Bowden, Principal of the Manchester College of Science and Technology, is profound for many reasons, not least for lending me a Copyflo enlargement of his microfilm of H. Wilmot Buxton's unpublished biography of Charles Babbage, in the Museum of the History of Science, Oxford.

I also pay tribute to Mr. R. H. Carruthers and the Directors of International Computers & Tabulators Ltd. for contributing a grant towards the cost of the research.

Sir John Murray, K.C.V.O., D.S.O., was especially helpful. I also thank Sir Shane Leslie, Bart., and Mr. Peter Dickinson of *Punch*.

Of friends who assisted me I should like to thank Annette Hornby, whose interest was invaluable, particularly at the beginning, when there were special difficulties connected with the writing of this book; Mavis MacKinnon, for so patiently and intelligently searching some of the documents for me, and for transcribing many of those in Part Three; and Vera Watson, for reading the typescript and for making various helpful suggestions.

Extracts from Charles Babbage's correspondence in the Department of Manuscripts of the British Museum are published by courtesy of the Trustees of the British Museum; Dr. C. H. Josten kindly allowed me to quote from the Buxton collection of Babbage manuscripts in the Museum of the History of Science, Oxford; while unpublished Crown Copyright material in the Public Record Office has been reproduced by permission of the Controller of H.M. Stationery Office.

Members of the following universities contributed very helpful information, for which I thank them: A. G. Lee, M.A., Librarian, St. John's College, Cambridge; J. H. P. Pafford, M.A., F.S.A., F.L.A., Goldsmith Librarian, London; Dr. E. J. Burge, Physics Department, King's College, London; Thomas Kelly, M.A., Director of External Mural Studies, Liverpool; Henry Parris, M.A., PH.D., Department of Extra Mural Studies, Sheffield; A. Jeffreys, University College, Keele, North Staffordshire.

Other librarians to whom I am indebted are L. L. Arden, F.L.A., Manchester College of Science and Technology; Miss Elizabeth Bower, *Punch*; G. Chandler, M.A., PH.D., F.L.A., F.R. HIST.S., City of Liverpool; D. Alasdair Kemp, Royal Observatory, Edinburgh; F. C. Tighe, B.A., F.L.A., City of Nottingham.

So many people performed some useful service for me that if I have inadvertently omitted some of their names I extend my heartfelt apologies: Herr Rolf Brück, H. G. F. Buckton, F. W. Cousins, P. Denison, J. Evans, C. H. Glover, M.A., W. S. Hunt, J. G. Hurst, M. C. Jones, E. Kersley, R. Lister, F. Maddison, C. W. Packham, M. P. Smith, R. N. Thomas, G. S. Wilkinson, Miss Frances J. Woodward, W. S. Yates.

Finally, I commend my secretary, Lynda Blayney, for so efficiently, intelligently and speedily typing the final draft.

M.M.

London 1964

Contents

*

PART THREE

PART FOUR

Illustrations

*

Author's Note

*

WHERE notes and sources are not given in the text they appear at the end of the book in sequence for each chapter. Many quotations are taken from *Passages from the Life of a Philosopher*, and no references appear. Again, for brevity's sake, Charles Babbage is denoted by his initials only, likewise the Countess of Lovelace.

The hitherto unpublished sources are, however, given in full. These include the twenty-three volumes of Charles Babbage's correspondence in the Department of Manuscripts of the British Museum; available letters and documents in the Lovelace Papers; H. Wilmot Buxton's unpublished biography in the Museum of the History of Science, Oxford; private communications from Mr. Richard H. Babbage. Of considerable value, also, was the privately printed *Memoirs and Correspondence of Major-General Henry P. Babbage*.

The reader who is interested in the purely scientific and technical aspects is referred to *Charles Babbage and his Calculating Engines*, by Philip and Emily Morrison, in which are reprinted the full text of General Menabrea's paper, with Lady Lovelace's notes, together with other technical publications by Charles Babbage and others, as well as a full list of Charles Babbage's published works, numbering about eighty. Those who wish to consult his mathematical library will find it at the Royal Observatory, Edinburgh. Much of Charles Babbage's correspondence was on purely mathematical subjects and this has not been consulted.

M.M.

Foreword

by B. V. Bowden, M.A., PH.D., M.SC.TECH., M.I.E.E.
Principal, the Manchester College of Science and Technology

*

*D*URING the last few years many people have become interested in the lives of the engineers and scientists of the last
century, and we have learned how some of the greatest engineering works of all time came to be built in England by men
who by any standards must be accounted among the most
imaginative, the most far-sighted and the most influential who
have ever lived. Among this extraordinary galaxy of talent
Charles Babbage appears to be one of the most remarkable of
all. Most of his life he spent in an entirely unsuccessful attempt
to make a machine which was regarded by his contemporaries
as utterly preposterous, and his efforts were regarded as futile,
time-consuming and absurd. In the last decade or so we have
learnt how his ideas can be embodied in a modern digital computer. He understood more about the logic of these machines
than anyone else in the world had learned until after the end of
the last war.

He was one of the first men to appreciate the potentialities
of the scientific method as applied to the problems of modern
industry. He lamented the way in which ordinary scientists
neglected their social obligations and industry was deaf to the
claims of scientific ideas. He was probably one of the most far-
sighted men of his generation, but almost everything he did
provoked derision and the scorn of nearly all his contemporaries.
This book shows us why he was so unsuccessful. He must have

15

been one of the queerest fish who ever lived. It is difficult to tell whether it was his oddities which were responsible for his failure, or his failure which made him odd! but this account of his life and his struggles, of his ideas, of his ambitions and of his failures, as well as of his successes, is absorbingly interesting and throws a most lurid light on the difficulties with which pioneers had to struggle a hundred years ago.

Charles Babbage was a man born out of his time and it is interesting to speculate if his life would have been any happier had he lived today. The reader must judge for himself.

Miss Moseley has studied all the relevant documents, including Babbage's correspondence, and has written a most comprehensive account of this talented and tormented man. He was lively enough in his youth, but shortly before his death he told a friend that he could not remember a single completely happy day in his life. 'He spoke as if he hated mankind in general, Englishmen in particular and the English Government most of all.' Many of his ideas are beginning to dominate our own society. He had genius, he was the affectionate friend of one of the most beautiful and talented women of his time—no less a person than Lord Byron's daughter—who was one of the very few people who understood him, but I think he was born to be miserable!

One is torn between admiration for his genius and pity for his wretchedness. But what a man.

B. V. BOWDEN

Manchester

ADDENDUM

Since this book was set up in type a life peerage has been conferred on Dr. Bowden, who has taken the title of Baron Bowden of Chesterfield. This honour is of special interest to the reader of this book, because Charles Babbage was an early and ardent advocate of peerage for life.

M.M.

Prologue

THE MAN

*

*I*T WAS in 1812 or 1813 that the handsome twenty-one-year-old Charles Babbage first thought of constructing an automatic machine that would fulfil the prime condition of performing its calculations and recording the result without the possibility of human errors creeping in. He was to spend the rest of his life—and he lived to be nearly eighty—trying to carry out this idea in metal. On paper he succeeded.

At least three of the most eminent authorities on the electronic digital computer have drawn attention to this pioneer work: the late Alan M. Turing, F.R.S., originator of the pilot ACE, Professor D. R. Hartree, F.R.S., and Dr. B. V. Bowden, who emphasized that Charles Babbage's ideas had begun to be properly appreciated only during the Second World War.

A perfectionist, Charles Babbage finished neither of his calculating machines, though parts of both were put together and are now in the Science Museum, London, S.W.7. He spent £20,000 of his private fortune on these and other scientific projects, and successive administrations made grants totalling £17,000.

The basic though not the only reason why they were not completed may be found in Sir Robert Peel's remark to his friend John Wilson Croker: 'I should like a little previous consideration before I move in a thin house of country gentlemen a large vote for the creation of a wooden man to calculate tables from the formula $x^2 + x + 41$. I fancy Lethbridge's face on being called to contribute.'

If the times had been more propitious it is probable that the difference engine would have been completed and the analytical engine begun; and that Charles Babbage would not have ended his life notorious for misanthropy and bitter hatred of his countrymen. But he was born over a century before his time, so it is not surprising that he was hopelessly misunderstood.

Yet he was himself only too well aware of the ignorance and obstructive attitude of the Lethbridges of this world. He had made attempt after attempt to explain in language comprehensible to them what he was trying to do, and had failed, lamentably; yet was always pathetically grateful when anyone showed the slightest interest or willingness to learn, regardless of the barrier, the difficulty of communication, between them.

This barrier between the Lethbridges and the Babbages is still, as we know, a very real one, in spite of Lord Hailsham's assertion that he has always resisted the idea of two cultures, the literate and the numerate, believing that only one culture exists, 'one corpus of knowledge, a vast continuum of information comprising many specialities'.

While this is certainly true in an ideal sense, it takes no account of what happens at a more practical level, and happened a hundred years ago, long before the days of specialization or before Sir Charles Snow delivered the 1959 Rede Lecture. The situation must have been infinitely worse at that time, when the electron had yet to be discovered, the atom to be split, before celestial exploration had become a race between the two greatest military powers on earth, when there was not even a motor-car in existence, nor a telephone, nor a typewriter.

One has only to glance back over the last few years to recall the violent opposition towards automation and the electronic digital computer to understand the Lethbridges of a century ago; for what Babbage was doing was to anticipate the fundamental principles on which the modern computer is based. The end was the same—only the means was different, limited by the materials available at the time.

Arithmetic, Charles Babbage had demonstrated, was

merely a matter of wheels, racks and springs. Brass and iron could carry out what had hitherto been regarded as the prerogative of the human brain. He had taught mechanism to think, or, at least, to carry out the processes of thought. This triumph of mind over matter was so far beyond the range of human experience that it was received with doubt, hesitation, incredulity and ridicule. Most people simply could not believe in the possibility of such an achievement, and this incredulity prevailed among all classes of society.

It was a sobering, a shocking, thought. There were those who considered the whole idea sacrilegious, regardless of the fact that it was not Charles Babbage's fault if the human brain were so constituted that some of its activities could be simulated by a machine.

Others insisted that there was nothing new in the idea of a calculating machine. While this was true of machines of very limited scope and power, it was not true of Babbage's inventions, especially the analytical engine, which, to quote Buxton, 'combines together *general* symbols in successions of unbounded variety and extent and forms a marvellous link of connection between the operations of matter and the most abstract conceptions of mind. Although it creates nothing, it develops a powerful language for the future of analysis, whereby the laws of the universe and their consequences may be traced in a manner hitherto unobtainable. The theoretical and practical will hereafter run side by side and be brought into more intimate connection with each other.'

It was useless to insist that it was a fundamental principle, basic to the whole system of mechanical computation, that the machine, although automatic, was incapable of originating thought or discovery or of dealing with data where the laws of a problem were not previously known. It merely added to the confusion for the inventor to explain his reason for using anthropomorphic terms:

'In substituting mechanism for the performance of operations hitherto executed by intellectual labour, it is continually necessary to speak of contrivances by which certain alterations in parts of the machine enable it to execute or to refrain from executing, particular functions. The analogy between these acts and the operations of mind almost forced upon me the figurative employment of the same terms. They were found at once convenient and expressive, and I prefer to continue their use rather than to substitute lengthened circumlocutions. For instance, "the engine *knows* &c." means that one out of many possible results of its calculations has happened, and that certain changes in its arrangement have taken place, by which it is compelled to carry out the next computation in a certain appointed way.'

Elsewhere he said: 'If at the time of the first carriage the engine *knew* the next number to which it was about to carry was a nine, and that consequently it would *afterwards* become necessary to give notice of, and carry, another ten, then it might be *taught* to execute both these carriages at the same time, and consequently to anticipate the time of the second carriage.'

All was confusion in the public mind, however, and Charles Babbage became an object of scorn and derision. He was criticized in scientific circles as well as by laymen, accused of deliberately procrastinating and delaying completion of the difference engine in order to obtain Government patronage for the much more powerful and spectacular analytical engine. He was even accused of pocketing the £17,000 from the Government, whereas the truth was the exact opposite, every penny having gone to the workmen engaged on the machine. From this sprang the bitterness that was to spoil his life.

In spite of it, however, he found time for numerous other activities, some of which are just as bewilderingly modern today as his calculating machines. This Titan of a man, as Dr. Bowden points out, was the originator of what is now known as operational research. He made acute analyses of the pin-making industry and the printing trade. He analysed the economics of the Post Office, as a result of which Sir Rowland Hill introduced the penny post. He studied insurance records and published the first comprehensive treatise on actuarial theory and the first reliable life tables. He invented the heliograph and the ophthalmoscope. He believed in miracles and in life peerages. He took a lifelong interest in ciphers and deciphering, and he could pick any lock. He wrote a ballet, and invented coloured lighting for the stage. He wished to write a novel, but was deterred, unhappily (for he could write very well) by Samuel Rogers, the banker poet. He stood for Parliament in the Liberal interest, and was perpetually at war with the Establishment. He pursued a vendetta with organ-grinders and street musicians, who disturbed his intellectual labours.

Contentious, contrary, sarcastic and cynical, there was another side to his character. The son of a rich London banker, he was no unapproachable scientific recluse hiding away in an ivory tower. He was a sociable, witty and lovable man, with a ringing, hearty laugh and an unfailing fund of amusing anecdotes on which he constantly dined out. Invitations to his own Saturday-evening parties were eagerly sought, the indispensable qualifications being intellect, beauty or rank. His son records that some 200 to 300 people would attend one of these gatherings, and that on one occasion no fewer than seven bishops were present.

For over forty years Charles Babbage was lionized by London society, and derived great pleasure from being lionized. Oddly enough, for a man of his intellectual attainments, this pleasure never palled. He knew everybody of note in the political, social, scientific, artistic and literary worlds of the day— such men as the Prince Consort, the Duke of Wellington, Laplace, Fourier, Alexander von Humboldt, the Herschels, Charles Darwin, John Stuart Mill, Dickens, Thackeray, Carlyle, Browning, Bulwer Lytton, Tennyson, Longfellow, Macready.

He was an excellent family man, a devoted son, brother, husband and father, though he seems to have anticipated the Victorians in one respect, believing that children—and wives, perhaps on occasion—should be seen and not heard. To the end of his long life, so far as all the available evidence shows, he remained faithful to the memory of his wife, who died at the early age of thirty-five, nine years before Victoria came to the throne. Yet he never once mentioned her in his autobiography.

As a widower he delighted in the friendship of educated

women. It was women who sustained him and exercised a soft-ening influence in some of the bitterest moments of his life. Two of his best friends were women—his mother and Augusta Ada, Countess of Lovelace, only child of Lord and Lady Byron: 'Ada, sole daughter of my house and heart.' Others were the Duchess of Somerset, the Baroness Burdett-Coutts and the Countess Harley-Teleki, who acted as intermediary between himself and L. F. Menabrea, the Italian mathematician and politician. These friendships lasted for years. There were times, in fact, when he seemed to be surrounded by princesses, duchesses, countesses and—parrots; not always, however, in order of precedence.

Unlike many mathematicians, he had no ear for music. 'The nightingales say you must write to them but (as you can't sing and hate music) I wonder how you will manage to send them any intelligible song', wrote Lady Lovelace in 1848. A mathe-matician of genius herself, she was also an accomplished musi-cian.

Yet in spite of his gay social life Charles Babbage was not a happy man. Tireless and restless, with a highly original, questioning mind, full of ideas which poured out in a contin-uous flow, he was probably his own worst enemy.

'I know intuitively that his passions and his better nature are tearing him to pieces—is there no voice to say to him—"Be still"?' Thus Lady Noel-Byron who, like her daughter, Lady Lovelace, knew him well.

Proud and sensitive to an almost abnormal degree, he im-agined slights and offences so easily—and sometimes where none was intended—that in the end he seems to have had a persecution complex verging on the paranoiac. The Hon. Lionel Tollemache, who knew him only in old age, said that irritation at the real or supposed disparagement of the machine embittered his whole life, and that he spoke as though he hated mankind in general, England in particular and the English Government and organ-grinders most. Yet, paradoxically, 'there was something harmless and even kindly in his misan-thropy, for (always excepting the musicians) he hated mankind rather than man, and his aversion was lost in its own generality'.

Shakespeare had described a similar character, Timon of Athens.

> 'I am sick of this false world, and will love nought
> But even the mere necessities upon 't.'

He held the Lucasian Chair of Mathematics at Cambridge —the Chair of Newton—for a number of years, saying that it was the only honour which he ever received in his own country. Although he declined at different times a knighthood and a baronetcy, he was notorious for craving honours and decorations. This was a serious and, for so great a man, a singular defect in his character.

Like many scientists, he was an optimist and a reformer, but, in the event, too forthright for politics. Although man, he believed, could never be made morally perfect, he could be much improved by the cultivation and taming of his instincts, and his higher aspirations diverted to objects less fraught with self-interest. In all his writings Charles Babbage revealed an instinctive desire to ameliorate the condition and promote the happiness of his fellow men, without realizing, apparently, that happiness is not necessarily conditional upon material prosperity and well-being.

While remaining cognizant of the imperfections of human nature, he invariably displayed a love of justice, but when injustice occurred, or when dishonesty or vain and empty pretension tried to pass for scholarship, then he would not hesitate, by the violence of his own criticism, to make enemies, or to risk charges of disloyalty or ingratitude, as occurred when he attacked the Royal Society and Sir Humphry Davy. It was not just a question of tactlessness. Monumental and deliberate were some of the rows which he provoked, and he stubbornly ignored all warnings and advice from his friends. He was not, in fact, a very subtle man.

There seems, too, to have been something lacking in his philosophy of life. It was perhaps a shade too facile. Just as the Lethbridges were out of sympathy with his view that everything could be reduced to equations, or 'number', as he expressed it, he was out of sympathy with their gods, the classical writers of Greece and Rome, even in old age dismissing such studies as of little importance except as exercises of the memory, contributing little to the material aspects of life. Insensitive to the beauties of Homer and the charms of Virgil, he was equally indifferent to the philosophical teaching of Aristotle and Plato, appreciative only of the paradoxical Bacon, whom he regarded as the founder of modern philosophy.

Buxton suggests that his dislike of Plato may have stemmed from that philosopher's condemnation of his contemporary Archytas, who had constructed machines of extraordinary power on mathematical principles. Such an application of the science of geometry, said Plato, was a degradation of a noble intellectual exercise, reducing it to the low level of a craft fit only for mechanics and artisans. And Buxton added that even Archimedes seemed half ashamed of having applied his ingenuity to any object of practical utility. The explanation of this attitude is, of course, that the Greeks had slaves, so had no need of labour-saving machinery.

It is thus possible that if Plato had encouraged, instead of discouraging, inventive and mechanical pursuits as unworthy of a philosopher, many revolutionary innovations, including the application of machinery to mathematical problems, might have been achieved centuries ago, instead of only in the last century and a half. Whether, in this case, mankind would have been any happier or wiser is beside the point here. It is, in any case, an unanswerable question.

Certainly Charles Babbage was no happier—the reverse, in fact. When he was an old man he would recall with immense pleasure the days of his youth, when life was free and buoyant, his friends faithful and sincere, when dreams had not been dissipated by reality or tinged with melancholy; when, above all, he had not become satiated by repletion.

If he had had more feeling for that most difficult of all studies, human nature—difficult because utterly unpredictable except on a statistical level, that is to say, in terms of manpower rather than of individuals and human beings—he might have been a happier and less disappointed man.

And if the Lethbridges had had more feeling for his world

then it might not have been necessary for him to say, as he did on one occasion, possibly weary of it all, 'it being sufficient merely to conceive that computations of great complexity can be effected by mechanical means'.

Part One
(1791-1827)

*

What should we think of a mechanism of wood and metal which not only computes astronomical and nautical tables to any degree of accuracy, but can also guarantee the mathematical accuracy of its observations by its own power of correcting possible errors? What are we to think of a mechanism that can not only do this, but can actually print the results of its complicated calculations as soon as they are obtained and perform all this without any intervention of human intelligence?

EDGAR ALLAN POE, *The Chess Player of Maelzel*

I

The Silver Lady

*

*F*ROM the very beginning Charles Babbage was a centre
of controversy. Even the date and place of his birth were no
exception. In extreme old age he wrote to the Statistical
Society: 'You may inform the French gentleman who made the
enquiry that the place of my birth was London and the year
was 1792.' But he was wrong. Either his memory failed him or
he had never known the truth, for he was born at Totnes,
Devonshire, on the 26th December 1791.

It was a memorable year, wholly in keeping with his own
turbulent character. Across the English Channel, the King of
France, the weak and vacillating Louis XVI, stung by daily
insults and wrongs, made a desperate attempt to escape from
his persecutors. Armed with a passport bearing a false name,
he set out with his Queen, Marie Antoinette, and his children
for the frontier town of Montmédy. Recognized at Varennes
by the postmaster Drouet, he was arrested and sent back, in
circumstances of the utmost humiliation, to Paris.

Farther east, war between Russia and Turkey had been going
on for three years. Austria, Sweden and Denmark were
involved, and the Prime Minister of England, the younger Pitt,
decided that the time had come to curb Russia's power. He
had several ships fitted up beyond the normal peace-time
establishment, and these were known as 'the Russian arma-
ment', but the measure was so unpopular that he had to defer
to public opinion and withdraw. The Russians, under their
Empress, Catherine II, and her favourite, Prince Potemkin,
pursued their aggression.

One of Catherine's most trusted and successful naval officers —he was known as the creator of the modern Russian Navy— was a Scot, Sir Samuel Greig, who had gone over to the Russian service and commanded the Baltic Fleet during the war. A son of his, later Russian Consul in London, was to marry Mary Fairfax, better known as Mary Somerville, mathematician, friend of Charles Babbage and the Countess of Lovelace.

In Birmingham the conflict between the friends and enemies of the French Revolution reached a crisis with a riot directed at Dr. Joseph Priestley, scientist, discoverer of oxygen, Unitarian and ardent fellow traveller, who had organized a public dinner to celebrate the 14th of July, the anniversary of the fall of the Bastille. Dr. Priestley's house was sacked, he lost his furniture, his scientific instruments and his MSS.

Into this tumultuous world, then, Charles Babbage was born. He was one of the two surviving children—the other was a sister who outlived him, the rest dying in infancy—of Benjamin Babbage, banker. His mother, née Betty Plumleigh Teape, like her husband, was a native of Totnes and descended from a well-known Devonshire family.

Although Charles always professed indifference to ancestors, saying that all that mattered was a man's published works, he mentioned several in his autobiography, *Passages from the Life of a Philosopher*. Remarking ironically that the name was 'unfortunately omitted' from the lists of the Conqueror's followers, he added that what he knew of his ancestors rested on a few documents and family tradition, mainly in the hands of a maiden aunt, the family historian.

In attempting to trace the origin of the name Babbage, he said that some people supposed that it derived from the cry of a sheep, others from the name of a place, Bab or Babb, in the West of England, such as Bab-Tor, Babbacombe. But this, he added, would not be possible, because the reverse was what actually happened—it was people who gave their names to barren places. On this, of course, he might have been challenged. Many Yorkshire people have derived their names from places —the termination 'royd', for example, as in Boothroyd and

Learoyd, being derived from the Norse or Scandinavian Riodr, which means a clearing in a forest.

Babbage was a not uncommon name in the West Country, and Charles recalls a grocer of Chudley who had adopted it because he thought it sounded better than his own name, Babb.

His ancestors seemed to have been engaged mostly in the craft of goldsmith, he said. Of actual individuals he mentioned several, notably one who married the daughter of Dr. Burthogge, a friend of John Locke. Another, in the time of Henry VIII, was taken prisoner at the siege of Calais. A third, a yeoman, possessing a small estate, undertook to distribute the proclamations of William III when the latter landed at Torbay, and for this treasonable act was rewarded with a silver medal, which descended to the maiden aunt, who showed it to her little nephew, Charles.

Another ancestor, an idle and dissipated young man named Richard Babbage, offended a wealthy relative, to whose large estates he was heir. This occurred about 1700 and the irate relative punished him by entailing the estates on eleven different people, making Richard the twelfth. Ten of them died, and the eleventh was dying of consumption, when Richard suddenly went off to America with Bamfylde Moore Carew, the Devonshire rector's son who ran away from school to join the gypsies, by whom he was elected king. Within twelve months of Richard's departure the eleventh in the entail died, the estates remaining in his representative's possession. If it could have been shown that Richard survived for twelve months the estates would have remained in Charles Babbage's branch of the family. And in 1773, when a part of this property had to be sold for the purpose of building a church at Ashbrenton, a private Act of Parliament was passed, preserving the rights of the true heir. But, although Benjamin Babbage advertised widely in American and European papers for proof of Richard's death, the reward was never claimed.

'I think myself very fortunate in thus having escaped the temptations as well as the duties of wealth. Even if I had resisted the former, long years of continuous intellectual labour would have entirely prevented me from fulfilling the latter', said

Charles with his tongue in his cheek, because at the age of thirty-six he inherited no less than £100,000 from his father, a vast fortune in those days, and a not inconsiderable sum in these. What he really should have said was that he never overcame his disappointment at not having been born into the aristocracy or, failing that, the landed gentry.

His father, Benjamin Babbage—the son of another Benjamin, who was Mayor of Totnes in 1754—was educated at King Edward VI Grammar School, Totnes, becoming subsequently managing partner of Praed, Mackworth & Babbage, London bankers.

Praed's, at 28 Fleet Street, unlike Child's Bank, no longer exists. Child's, still at 1 Fleet Street, was the original of Tellson's in *A Tale of Two Cities*, and its vaults were generally believed to contain numerous valuables deposited by the French *émigrés*. Praed's or, rather, its managing partner acquired a different kind of fame. Benjamin Babbage was the first man to lend money at five per cent interest and so became known as 'Old Five Per Cent'. He was an enlightened man, as well as a good man of business, making no attempt to influence Charles in his determination to become a scientist instead of a banker.

In 1801, as managing partner of Praed's, Benjamin lived with his family over the bank premises. Four years later, after the Battle of Trafalgar, he sold his partnership and moved to 5 Devonshire Street. He built another house at Teignmouth in Devonshire and named it The Rowdens, where he died in 1827.

In his later years Benjamin was haunted by the spectres of three women dressed in white. Writing in old age to Sir Benjamin Brodie, chemist and discoverer of graphitic acid, Charles recalled how his father was perfectly aware of the un-reality of these apparitions, and frequently discussed them. One day when Charles was reading to him his father stopped him by remarking that his 'phantoms' were appearing.

'Describe them,' said the analytically minded Charles.

'I distinctly see three women dressed in white sitting in chairs on the right-hand side of the room.'

There happened to be one chair at the place indicated, so Charles removed it. It made no difference to the apparitions.

He then placed other chairs in the same position, and put a dressing-gown and towels on them, arranging other objects to conceal any shapes in the wallpaper which might have been the foundation of what he called 'the mistake'. Still it made no difference. His father could still see three women in white. These visions continued for some years, but Benjamin was never afraid of them, only puzzled. The perfect clarity of the figures as seen by himself but invisible to everyone else struck him as remarkable.

'He soon however assigned the facts to some derangement of the optic nerve,' said Charles, dryly, 'and these visions gave him no further uneasiness.'

His mother, as is often the case with men of outstanding genius, was a remarkable woman. When her daughter-in-law died, and her son moved to 1 Dorset Street, she supervised and brought up all his children, so that he could pursue his studies undisturbed. And later, when in a moment of doubt about the analytical engine, knowing all the difficulties and the expense involved, Charles hesitated, she said: 'My dear son, you have advanced far in the accomplishment of a great object, which is worthy of your ambition. You are capable of completing it. My advice is, pursue it, even if it should oblige you to live on bread and cheese.'

It is not surprising that his mother occupied a unique place in Charles Babbage's affections. He was already a middle-aged man of fifty-three when she died, but the pain of parting from her was acute.

Brought up in the Protestant faith, the little boy was taught by this 'excellent mother' to pray night and morning. Neither of his parents was in the least bigoted or intolerant, nor, on the other hand, were they guilty of 'that unbecoming and familiar mode of addressing the Almighty which afterwards so much disgusted me in my youthful years'.

Like any modern mother, Mrs. Babbage impressed upon her small son the importance of taking care at street crossings. One day when he was about five years old he was crossing London Bridge with his nurse, who was carrying his infant brother in her arms. Charles, gazing enraptured at the ships in the river, turned at length to find himself alone. Quite unalarmed and full of self-possession, he proceeded as far as Tooley Street, where, remembering his mother's instructions, he awaited the opportunity to cross. Finally, the traffic abated, and he reached the other side in safety, pausing opposite a linen draper's shop.

Seeing the child alone, one of the shopmen came out and asked him what he wanted. Charles realized that he had lost his nurse. The shopman gave him some pears and told him to sit on the doorstep and eat them, meantime sending off a messenger to Mrs. Babbage, who happened to be one of his own customers. Thus she knew about her boy's recovery before she had heard of his loss, although the nurse had told the crier that a reward of five shillings would be paid for news of her charge. As the gold-laced functionary paraded up and down in front of him, the child was far too interested in his pears to be aware of the sensation he was causing.

Years later he was standing almost on the same spot when what he considered a strange coincidence occurred. A number of buildings was being demolished, and a large slate fell, missing him by inches. With characteristic technical love of detail, he said that this slate was one of the largest kind, called a duchess, adding that there was an aristocracy even among slates— 'perhaps from their occupying the most elevated position in a house'—ranging in size from ladies and countesses up to the largest, duchesses.

Once he ate some poisonous berries and, on returning home, was made to stand between his father's knees and swallow a dose of castor oil. Benjamin was seated beside the chimney-piece in the breakfast-room, beneath a picture of Christ taken down from the cross. Opposite was an interior of Antwerp Cathedral. The incident made such an impression on the child's mind that all his life he remembered every detail with the utmost clarity. To his astonishment, neither of his parents retained the slightest recollection of the incident.

As a child, Charles Babbage was extremely delicate, and his parents had great difficulty in rearing him. This in no way retarded his mental development. On the contrary, from his earliest years he displayed a curiosity that could almost be designated intellectual, far transcending the incessant questioning to which children subject their elders. Charles was not content to question. He *experimented*.

'Mamma, what is inside of it?' was his invariable demand when given a new toy. And until he had an answer he gave his elders no rest; and if he was not satisfied with the answer he would take the toy apart in order to satisfy his curiosity.

Even his interest in automata was discernible early in life. While still a boy he was taken by his mother to several exhibitions of machinery, one of which was held in Hanover Square by a man called Merlin. The boy was so manifestly fascinated by what he had seen that the exhibitor invited him up to his workshop. In the attic were two nude female figures in silver, about twelve inches in height. One of them glided forward for about four feet, then turned and retraced her steps. Sometimes she used an eyeglass, and, more often, bowed to invisible acquaintances of her own kind. The other was a dancer, on the forefinger of whose right hand was a bird, which wagged its tail, flapped its wings and opened its beak.

'This lady', says Charles, 'attitudinized in a most fascinating manner. Her eyes were full of imagination and irresistible.'

Irresistible she was, indeed. One of the pair, which he was to acquire in later years, proved an unfailing attraction to those of his guests at the Dorset Street parties who found themselves out of their depth when the difference engine came to be demonstrated. And who knows what influence she had in shaping the course of the boy's future career?

35

'My dear Charles'

*

*O*F THE hundreds upon hundreds of letters which Charles Babbage received and preserved during his lifetime all but one appear to begin, according to the writer's degree of intimacy with him, 'Dear Sir', 'Dear Mr. Babbage', 'My dear Babbage'. The exception is 'My dear Charles'. And the writer was Frederick W. Marryat, author of *Mr. Midshipman Easy*, *Masterman Ready* and *Children of the New Forest*.

There is something significant about this opening for it reflects the affection in which, in spite of his brilliance, he was held not only by Marryat but by all his school friends. Latent genius though he was from his early years, he was no dreary 'swot' or superior intellectual. In carrying out his 'experiments' he found willing allies; and in all his activities his perseverance and, above all, his originality, courage, gaiety and wit overcame all opposition. To all his school friends, and to all his friends throughout his life, he was a fascinating companion.

Soon after his eleventh year, and following a severe illness from which he nearly died, he was sent into the care of a clergyman at Alphington, near Exeter, his parents hoping that his native air would prove more beneficial than that of London. They expressly stated that the boy's brain was not to be taxed too much, and this instruction was so faithfully observed that Charles wasted most of his time, reflecting later that this 'great idleness may have led to some of my childish reasonings'.

Of these reasonings the supernatural formed an important element. Ghost stories and the idea of personal visitations from the devil were prevalent among his schoolfellows, and Charles, although having some doubts, tended on the whole to share these beliefs and was frankly terrified at the idea of any materialization. Aided by a companion, however, he frightened a bigger boy so thoroughly with some trick, such as casting shadows on a wall, that it occurred to him that he in turn might have been deluded by older people. So, with scientific exactitude, he gathered all the available information from the other boys, and found that the Prince of Darkness, according to written tradition, had become visible in a number of forms, including a rabbit, an owl, a black cat (very frequent), a raven and a man with a cloven foot (also frequent).

He dwelt much on this, believing it to be very wicked, but finally curiosity overcame his scruples. He told himself that all he desired was an interview with the gentleman to prove his existence. With remarkable courage, then, this child went alone at dusk to a deserted attic and closed the door. He thereupon cut his finger, and with the blood from the wound drew a circle on the floor. Standing in the centre of this circle, he read or recited the Lord's Prayer backwards, at first with trepidation and towards the end in absolute terror. He found himself transfixed, his heart pounding, gazing in horror from window to chimney, from chimney to window. Fortunately, no owl, or black cat or unlucky raven appeared, or, as he said, he might well, in his weak state of health, have died; or, at best, the spirit of enquiry might have been quelled for ever.

Gradually, his limbs unfroze, and he managed to move from the circle and leave the room, slowly, at first, then running with all his might. On rejoining his friends he said nothing. Later, in bed, he said his prayers silently to himself. Halfway through the Lord's Prayer he forgot a sentence and could not continue. This upset him so much that after repeating another prayer or hymn he lay awake for hours. 'I thought that this forgetfulness was a punishment inflicted upon me by the Almighty and that I was a wicked little boy for having attempted to satisfy myself about the existence of the devil.'

Although he managed to get through the Lord's Prayer on the following night, he was still uneasy. Doubts about the existence of the devil had led him to doubts about the Bible and the religion which asserted Lucifer to be a living being. His sense of justice suggested to him that it was impossible for an all mighty, all merciful, God to punish him, a poor little boy, with eternal damnation because he had so anxiously and sincerely tried to verify the truth or falsehood of the religion which he had been taught. He prayed to God to tell him the truth.

His characteristic reaction was to make an experiment. He decided that if at a certain hour of a certain day he went to a certain room in the house and found the door open he would believe the Bible; otherwise he would not. By the time he came to write his memoirs he had forgotten the state of the door, but concluded that it was open, because for many years afterwards he was no more troubled by religious doubts.

His interest in the supernatural continued, however. One of his school friends was a son of Admiral Richard Dacres, and the two boys agreed that the first to die should, if possible, appear to the other, in order to provide the answer to one of the questions that so tormented them. Dacres entered the Navy, but the two kept up their friendship. After serving in a ship of eighty guns under the command of Sir Thomas Duckworth at the passage of the Dardanelles, young Dacres was sent home in charge of a prize ship, under conditions of such extreme hardship that he contracted tuberculosis and died at the age of eighteen.

A few days before his death Charles saw him, and though neither mentioned the compact, it was in both their minds. On the night of his friend's death Charles sat up till midnight in his own room at The Rowdens, which was separated from the rest of the house by a conservatory. Overpowering curiosity prevented him from reading. He then examined the room to make certain that no bird or animal was concealed in it and (as he was to do some years later in the case of his father) took note of the furniture and other objects in case they should mislead him. He then undressed and got into bed. 'I passed a night of perfect sleeplessness. The distant clock and a faithful dog, just outside my own door, produced the only sounds which disturbed the intense silence of that anxious night.'

He derived more satisfaction from a different kind of

episode. One day, listless and unoccupied, he imagined that he had a headache. Supporting his head on his left arm, he leaned against a tree, and, looking down, saw a bright, glittering object. Picking it up, he believed it to be a gold coin of great value. In the excitement he forgot his headache. The coin turned out to be a half-dram weight from the box of a pair of medical scales belonging to the village doctor, but, said Charles, the experience taught him that intense concentration, on a novel such as *Don Quixote* or *Robinson Crusoe*, could cure, or make him forget, a moderate pain.

From Alphington he was sent to his father's old school, King Edward VI Grammar School, Totnes. This ancient foundation has an unbroken record going back to 1553, and in Charles's time had some day boys and an unspecified number of boarders, fees for the latter being £55 per annum. All the boys received a classical education, which could not have commended itself much to the future inventor of the calculating machines.

The school was in a seventeenth-century building on the Town Wall, adjoining the Guildhall, and occupied the second floor. There were four mullioned windows, the crevices of which had to be stuffed up with copybooks on cold and draughty winter days. In the playground, known in modern times as the Guildhall Yard, the boys played prisoners' base, and when the magistrates sat in the Guildhall they sneaked in and heard prisoners sentenced. Apart from Charles Babbage, the school has had several notable Old Boys, including A. S. M. Hutchinson, whose novel *If Winter Comes* was the phenomenal bestseller of 1921.

In spite of his poor health Charles made his mark—on one of the desks. As a visitor years later he pointed out the place where he had carved his name. And today the name is commemorated in more adult form—Babbage House.

The cold and the draughts were too much for him, and he spent the next year or two at home, idling about under the fitful tuition of private tutors. But as adolescence approached his health improved and he was sent to the academy of the Rev. Stephen Freeman, at Forty Hill, Enfield, Middlesex, where he was to remain for three years. Among the thirty boys was

Frederick Marryat, who in after life 'loved to recall that of all the boys at his private school the dame had singled out himself and Babbage as the two who were not only bad, but would never get on in the world'.

His introduction to this seminary was not very happy. An unfair trick was played upon him and he never forgot it. Seeing what he imagined to be two trespassers in a master's orchard, Charles, with a companion, gave chase. Having caught up with the intruders at a ditch, they were greeted by loud peals of laughter. The trespassers were schoolfellows who, seeking manure for their flowers, had guessed what was happening and lured them on. When Charles and his friend tried to explain to the master that they had been acting in his interests he would not listen and fined each of them one shilling.

It was at Enfield that the bigger boys made ciphers. Charles had to know only a few words to be able to find the key. For this he was sometimes thrashed—though the fault, as he says, 'lay in their own stupidity'. This interest in ciphers was to continue throughout his life.

The school possessed an excellent library of 300 volumes, among them a treatise on algebra, *Ward's Young Mathematician's Guide*. Charles was entranced by this, and after he had been at the school for about a year made a practice of rising at 3 a.m. with a companion, and, having lit a fire in the school-room, working until 5 or 5.30 a.m.

This went on for several months and then a bigger boy asked to join them, saying that his sole object was to study and that it would be of great benefit to him in after life. Charles refused, and for ever afterwards regretted his churlishness. Frederick Marryat made the same request. Charles replied that as the other wished only to play, they would be found out, so again he refused. Marryat was of a more mettlesome temperament, however, and replied that he was determined to get up, and would do it in spite of Charles.

The two of them shared a bedroom with three other boys, and a battle of wits commenced. One night Charles found it impossible to open the door. Marryat had pushed his bed forward and blocked it so that Charles could not go out without awakening him. Charles pushed the bed carefully back and went to work. The same thing happened again. Then he found a piece of pack-thread tied to the lock, assuming that it was attached to Marryat's arm or hand again in order to rouse him. He untied the cord and went downstairs. A few nights later the cord could not be untied, so had to be cut with a penknife. Each successive night the cord became thicker and thicker—and was followed by a small chain, which Charles manipulated with a pair of pliers. But then there were stouter chains, and a padlock which he could not pick in the dark. So Marryat won. And, as Charles had predicted, no work was done. Fireworks were let off in the playground, ending in discovery and punishment.

Another escapade started when a Russian parlour-border told Marryat about the joys of cognac. One evening Marryat came to Charles with a 'quart bottle of what he called excellent stuff'. Charles was not greatly impressed but thought it might be better if mixed with treacle. There was a whip round for the treacle and the mixture was put into a large plant-pot, the hole in its base being stopped up with a cork. All the nauseous brew had been consumed when the bell rang for prayers. Decorum prevailed until the end and then:

'Many boys rose up from their knees—but some fell down again. Some turned round several times, and then fell. Some turned round so often that they resembled spinning dervishes. Others were only more stupid than usual; some complained of being sick; many were very sleepy; others were sound asleep, and had to be carried to bed; some talked fast and heroically, two attempted psalmody, but none listened.'

There was nothing else for it but send them off to bed immediately. Little else seems to have been done, investigation proving fruitless. Beyond the fact that 'Count Cogniac [sic] had married the sweet Miss Treacle' no one—boys or, apparently, masters—said a word. 'I believe neither the pedigree of the bridegroom nor his domicile were ever discovered. It is probable that he was of French origin, and dwelt in a cellar.'

Other escapades, or 'experiments', one of which nearly cost him his life, occurred during the holidays when he was about sixteen. The Rowdens stood on the cliffs near Teignmouth, the grounds extending to the sea. Access to the beach was comparatively easy and this gave Charles a taste for swimming and bathing. One Christmas, desirous of knowing whether he could manage a gun, he took his father's fowling-piece and, after firing a few charges, hit a diver. The bird fell into the sea. The sea was rough and snow was falling, so in the absence of a dog or a boat, Charles undressed, swam out and retrieved his game, which, being roasted subsequently by the cook, proved extremely unpalatable. Sea-birds, he decided, were better left alone. Not so water.

Soon afterwards, after many immolations in the River Dart, he tried to devise a means of walking on water, the idea being 'to attach to each foot two boards closely connected by hinges, themselves fixed to the sole of the shoe'. These boards, according to the theory, would close up together when the leg was raised as in walking. When lowered, pressure of the water between the boards would make a flat surface, offering greater resistance to the wearer's sinking. He cut up a couple of heavy tomes with very thick bindings and fixed them by hinges to a pair of boots, placing wedges between the two flaps of each book, in order to keep them apart and prevent the pressure of water from opening them. Thus equipped, Charles walked into the water and started to swim.

He now tried the 'grand experiment', and, by using his legs, kept his head and shoulders and, at times, his arms above water. With very little effort he managed to retain himself in a vertical position as he floated down the river with the receding tide. Then one of the pair of hinges failed him. He became lopsided. He had to strike out and it was very hard going. Other difficulties occurred. He had to swim in a spiral, but struggled into a vertical position. Still struggling, his feet touched bottom and he reached the bank, totally exhausted. He decided that in future he would trust to his own unaided powers when in the water.

About this time he first realized the full significance of the Athanasian Creed. It seemed to him a direct contradiction in terms and frequent recourse to the prayer book gave him little comfort, likewise to his elders, who assured him that it was all true and part of the Christian religion, and that it was wicked of him to doubt it. He simply could not believe it, and felt much alarmed, feeling that if it were an essential dogma he could not belong to that faith.

To the end of his life he felt the same about it. If three things could be one thing, he argued, then the whole science of arithmetic was at once annihilated, and the laws which governed the solar system, as astronomers had shown, were mere dreams. If, on the other hand, it was attempted to show a mystic sense in which three and one were the same thing, then all language 'through which alone man can exert his reasoning faculty becomes useless, because it contradicts itself and is untrue'.

From Enfield he went to a clergyman near Cambridge, who was probably a crammer, for Charles was one of only six boys and 'did not derive from it all the advantage that I might have done'. He often met the Rev. Charles Simeon, the Evangelical divine, and every Sunday had to write abstracts of the day's sermons. He then thought he would write one of his own, based on the text 'Alexander the coppersmith hath done us much harm'. This somehow got into the hands of authority. This time something was said and, presumably, done.

The observant boy noted, however, that by an exchange of sermons between the Rev. Mr. Simeon and his own tutor only half the number otherwise required by each had to be written —a striking illustration, as he says, of the economy of manufactures, as well as providing variety, 'which, when moderately indulged in, excites the appetite'.

The time was now approaching when he would have to go to the University, however, and to this end he lived for a time at Totnes with an Oxford tutor, who supervised his classical studies.

In mathematics, however, he was so far advanced that his wide reading was to have important repercussions for him as an undergraduate. In spite of all the gaiety, pranks and experiments, his intellectual curiosity, coupled with his intense power of concentration, had already made him familiar with the work of the Continental mathematicians of the time, who were far in advance of their British contemporaries. In later life he often referred to Ward's *Young Mathematician's Guide* as the first book to rouse his interest in analytical investigation. Other books which had already come his way were Humphrey Ditton's *Fluxions*, Maria Agnesi's *Analytical Institutions*, Woodhouse's *Principles of Analytical Calculation*, Lagrange's *Theorie des Fonctions* and the works of Maclaurin and Thomas Simpson.

3

The Dot-age of the University

*

*I*N OCTOBER 1810, when he was nearly nineteen years old,
Charles Babbage was entered at Trinity College, Cambridge,
whence, said Buxton, 'he migrated to Peterhouse, taking his
degree in 1814'.

His reason for transferring to Peterhouse in his third year was
his conviction that he would be beaten in the Tripos examinations by his friends John Herschel and George Peacock, and
preferred to be first at Peterhouse rather than third at Trinity.
In the event he was first at Peterhouse.

The sudden transition to the comparatively free and easy life
of the University filled him with joy. He now felt himself to be
a man. Deference, unknown to him as a schoolboy, was now
paid to him. He had an allowance of £300 a year, and formed
the habit of drawing £30 at a time. Entries in his personal
account book show that he constantly gave away money, a few
shillings at a time, from week to week, to anyone who spun
him a hard-luck yarn, as he sometimes later found out. There
is a note at the end of one year's entries which reads: 'This
balance differs 1/6 from Messrs. Praed's. Most probably mine
is wrong.'

Like most other undergraduates, he found it difficult to
resist the temptation offered by Cambridge tradesmen to live
beyond his means. The practice of giving unlimited credit to
the sons of rich fathers was one that only the strongest-minded
could resist—Charles Babbage seems on the whole to have
resisted well, although to quote his own words: 'I lived probably
in a greater variety of sets than any of my young companions.

45

But my chief and choicest consisted of some ten or a dozen friends who usually breakfasted with me every Sunday after chapel; arriving at about nine, and remaining to between twelve and one o'clock. We discussed all knowable and many unknowable things.'

These sets reflected the wide variety of his own interests, his versatility and his high spirits.

There was the Ghost Club, whose investigations proved interesting and instructive. There was the Extractors' Club, one of whose rules insisted that if after a period of twelve months a member had failed to communicate his address, it was to be taken for granted that he had been shut up as insane, when 'every effort legal and illegal shall be made to get him out of the madhouse. Hence the name of the club—The Extractors.'

Another set consisted of first-class chess-players, one of whom was the son of Madame d'Arblay, otherwise Fanny Burney. Another member named Brande devoted practically all his time to the study of chess. He was so good that Charles's only chance of winning was to make so bad a move early in the game that it would never have occurred to his opponent to believe such ignorance possible.

Yet another set, which included a future tutor of Trinity, a budding Attorney General and a potential 'learned and accomplished Dean' played sixpenny whist. At Jesus College he mixed with other whist addicts, but while they played for guinea points and five guineas on the rubber, he never played more than shilling points and five shillings on the rubber, which made him very popular because, he said, his partner had what was considered to be an advantage—that of playing guinea points with one of their opponents and pound points with the other.

Sailing—but not the 'manual labour of rowing'—was another of his favourite pastimes. He kept 'a beautiful light, London-built' boat, and would sometimes embark on long trips down the river beyond Ely into the fens, sometimes as far as King's Lynn. In case the wind failed or was contrary, he took with him two or three hefty rowing men, who were unkindly described by the more intellectual members of the Ghost Club as Charles's 'Tom fools'.

Charles's plan of campaign on these expeditions was to send his servant to the apothecary for a certificate, saying that he was indisposed and incapable of attending chapel, hall or lectures. The servant then proceeded to ask the cook to prepare 'a large well-seasoned meat pie, a couple of fowls &c. These were packed in a hamper with three or four bottles of wine and one of noyeau'. Sailing, fishing and shooting on Whittlesea Mere provided plenty of sport and exercise, and after five or six days of this carefree life the party returned refreshed in mind and body.

Although of secondary interest, he spent some of his time at Cambridge attending the lectures of Smithson Tennant, professor of chemistry, and, having a spare room, turned it into a laboratory, in which John Herschel worked with him for a time. Charles was much upset when Smithson Tennant was accidentally killed while riding with General Bulow at Boulogne.

His major interest is perhaps best symbolized by the reply of a tutor of one of the colleges when consulted by Benjamin Babbage: 'Advise your son not to purchase his wine in Cambridge.' The gentleman might well have added: 'Advise your son not to expect any help in the study of the calculus at Cambridge.' In other words, the Cambridge of that time was not the best place for Charles to continue those studies on which he had embarked at school, and this was to prove a source of life-long disappointment.

He could at this time work out questions with equal facility 'in the dots of Newton, the ds of Leibniz or the dashes of Lagrange', but had found many problems and was eagerly looking forward to having them solved. In 1811, passing through London on his way to Cambridge, he paid seven guineas for a copy of Lacroix's great work on the Differential and Integral Calculus. On reaching his destination he spent most of the night browsing over his purchase. Two or three days later he asked his tutor Hudson to explain some of his difficulties, but was told that these questions would not be asked in the Senate House, and were therefore of no consequence. On a second and a third occasion he asked for help, with the same negative result.

Mathematical training at the University consisted at this time in taking some part of the *Principia* of Newton, or perhaps some other writer, and this the candidate for honours was to study to the exclusion of all else, like a child with his lesson. He was to commit it to memory in order to answer the questions that would be put to him. And while it was the genius of Newton which had led to further discoveries by foreign mathematicians, insular prejudice, or misguided loyalty to Newton, still caused them to be ignored in Newton's own country.

Thus Buxton points out that in his great edition of Newton's works, published in 1785, Dr. Samuel Horsley, Bishop of St. Asaph and Fellow of the Royal Society, made no mention of the three bodies, nor of the perturbations of the planetary motions, nor of the law whereby the stability of the universe was secure. Yet Clairant, d'Alembert and Euler had published their solutions of the problem of the three bodies in 1747; and Lagrange had demonstrated in 1776 that the changes in the orbits of the planets were periodic.

Apart from being behind the times, and grossly unscientific in its insularity or loyalty (or perhaps simply lazy), the tutorial system of that day killed all originality of thought and enterprise, and Charles Babbage decided that if he were to succeed in what really interested him he must rely upon his own exertions, and to concentrate on a subject which had not so far attracted much attention in England; namely, the theory of functional equations of all orders.

He therefore made a profound study of the papers of Euler and other authorities, which he found in the volumes of the academies of St. Petersburg, Berlin and Paris. Next he proposed to found a society to promote his interests, this being the occasion for one of his wittiest sallies. A fierce controversy was going on at the time. Societies had been formed for printing and circulating the Bible, one party proposing to circulate it with notes in order to make it more intelligible, the other rejecting this as profane, the word of God being perfect. He drew up a plan of the proposed society, parodying one of the broadsheets of the Bible controversy, proposing that periodical meetings should be held for the propagation of ds, and consigning to perdition all who supported the heresy of dots, at the same time maintaining that the work of Lacroix was so perfect that comment was superfluous.

He gave the parody to a friend, Michael Slegg, of Trinity, who passed it on to another mathematical friend, Edward Bromhead (afterwards Sir Edward French Bromhead, Bart.). As a result a meeting was held for the purpose of forming a society for the promotion of analysis, those present, in addition to the promoters, including John (later Sir John) Herschel, son of Sir William, George Peacock, later Dean of Ely, D'Arblay, son of Fanny Burney, Edward (later Sir Edward) Ryan, Chief Justice of Calcutta and Charles Babbage's brother-in-law, and Frederick Maule, younger brother of Mr. Justice Maule.

In this way the Analytical Society came into being. A room was hired, meetings were held, papers written, read and discussed. In spite of ridicule from the dons, the society prospered even to the extent of publishing a volume of *Transactions*, which, owing to illness or other causes, was entirely the work of Charles Babbage and John Herschel. The moment came to choose a title. It would have been asking too much of Charles not to suggest 'The Principles of Pure D-ism in opposition to the Dot-age of the University'.

One evening he was sitting in the room of the Analytical Society, half dreaming, with a table of logarithms lying open before him, when another member came in and seeing him half asleep said: 'Well, Babbage, what are you dreaming about?' He replied, indicating the logarithms: 'I am thinking that all these tables might be calculated by machinery.'

Some years were to pass before he returned to this idea, and in the meantime he decided to translate Lacroix's smaller treatise on the calculus. The idea, he said, might have occurred to other members of the Analytical Society, but they were occupied with their degree or examinations for fellowships. He was the exception and therefore started the task, but eventually had to put it aside, half finished, and it remained untouched for some time, when the rest was jointly translated by Herschel and Peacock, and published in 1816. It contained notes of their own and an appendix, mainly, if not wholly, by Herschel, on finite differences.

'The importance of this step cannot be exaggerated', said Buxton; 'it broke down barriers of national prejudice which had long cramped and paralysed the energies and enterprise of the University, and created an epoch of thought which in a few years entirely revolutionized the ancient system of University teaching.'

This statement hardly conveys the amount of time and labour spent not only on the translation but also upon a textbook, *Examples to the Differential and Integral Calculus*, also a joint production, published in 1820. To this Charles contributed an essay on the solution of functional equations. A vast correspondence on these subjects, continuing from 1810 to 1817, was carried on between Charles Babbage, Herschel, Maule, Bromhead and others. The two following examples sum it all up as far as Charles was concerned.

Writing in August 1811, from Teignmouth, to his friend Higman, afterwards a tutor of Trinity, he said:

'Last Sunday week I began a letter to you explaining an hypothesis respecting functions, before I got half through the letter I observed an error which obliged me to commit my letter to the flames, and my system to oblivion. I began a second letter and a second system which was founded on sounder principles; this I supported by an example, but oh, the perverseness of things! the example completely confuted the system, nor could the most refined analytical tortures reduce the refractory formulae to obedience to the parent system.'

Four years later, on 26th November 1815, he was much happier about it all, for he wrote from Devonshire Street to John William Whittaker, Fellow of St. John's College, Cambridge:

'I send you a copy of a paper of mine on functions on which subject I am decidedly mad without the remotest possibility of a cure, seeing that it is so fertile in beautiful results that it might well occupy half a dozen lives without being near exhausted. I have received some excellent remarks on them from Bromhead, who is also a little touched.'

In these studies germinated the seeds of his ideas for performing mathematical operations by machinery. But before there was any practical outcome he married and begot a large family.

4

Georgiana

*

WHILE at Cambridge, presumably, and possibly through his friend Edward Ryan, Charles Babbage met his future wife, Georgiana. She was a daughter of William Whitmore, of Dudmaston, Co. Salop, whose family had been proprietors of Apley and the greater part of Bridgnorth for centuries. ·

There were two branches of this county family, the other residing at Orsett Hall, Essex. Georgiana's branch, known as the Wolryche Whitmores, was descended on the distaff side through many noble families from Joan Beaufort, daughter of Edward III's son, John of Gaunt, by his mistress and third wife, Catherine Swynford, Duchess of Lancaster. Georgiana's portrait, done in her early twenties, shows a charming young woman dressed in the Empire style. Judging from a lock of her hair, given to her son by his aunt, Mrs. Hollier, in 1855, and still in the possession of her great-grandson, it was a glorious golden-brown, and seems as bright and colourful today as it must have appeared on its owner's head 150 years ago.

The marriage took place in June 1814, the year in which the bridegroom took his degree, and exactly one year before the Battle of Waterloo—he was to see Napoleon on board the *Bellerophon* in Torbay. Charles was twenty-three years old and Georgiana was twenty-two. In November of that year they went to live at Benjamin Babbage's house at 5 Devonshire Street, and there Charles established a workshop on the upper floor of the coach house.

The story of Charles Babbage's married life is one of almost unrelieved sadness. It was to produce eight children in thirteen years, ending with Georgiana's death at the age of thirty-five. Of these eight children only three sons, Herschel, Dugald and Henry, survived to maturity, four dying in infancy or childhood, the only daughter surviving to her late teens.

Georgiana must have been, and almost certainly was, entirely submissive to her husband. She could not have lived with him otherwise. He was not only an exacting man of genius but also a man of superhuman energy, who would retire to his library and, with a similar degree of concentration, sit over a problem for hours, when the crying and prattling of young children must have been utterly and completely forbidden anywhere within earshot. Even the workshop above the coach house, where he was already constructing, or supervising the construction of, models of parts of the difference engine, his wife must have hesitated to approach.

Her mother-in-law, too formidable, possessive and immensely proud of her son, must have been a trial. Georgiana's own youngest surviving son, Henry, who was only three when his mother died, was afraid of his grandmother and of his father, though later in life he became deeply attached to Charles. As a child and a young man, however, he so feared him that he often left the house to avoid meeting him. It is clear, on the other hand, that in his own odd way Charles adored his wife and children, and was utterly unaware of the unhappy impression he was creating.

Some of his experiments at this time were as far-sighted as they must have been trying to his wife. The young couple were regularly receiving supplies of game from a relative in the country, but the carriage was so excessive that butcher's meat would have been less expensive. So, while Georgiana interested herself in the culinary side, he burrowed away until he learned why the charge was so high, suggesting that if the Government, through the Post Office, were to undertake the task of verification and become book- and parcel-carriers, much profit would accrue to them, with benefit to the public. This idea preceded those of Sir Rowland Hill, and was mentioned in *The Economy of Manufactures*.

He then concluded that a uniform rate of postage for letters would be more economical, because the cost of transporting a letter, no matter how far, was negligible compared with the cost of collection and distribution. Not content with this he carried out experiments which must have considerably disordered Georgiana's social activities:

'I then devised means for transmitting letters enclosed in small cylinders, along wires suspended from posts, and from towers, or from church steeples. I made a little model of such an apparatus, and thus transmitted notes from my front drawing-room, through the house, into my workshop, which was in a room above my stables.'

In 1818 he went down in a diving bell at Plymouth. It was a cast-iron vessel, about 5 ft. long by 4½ ft. wide by 5 ft. 8 in. high, with seats for four people.

This experience roused his interest in submarine navigation, and in the article on the diving bell which he contributed to the 1826 edition of the *Encyclopaedia Metropolitana* he described an open submarine vessel which would contain enough air for four people for more than two days. He was not the originator of this idea: experiments had already been made in the Seine at Paris, and Fulton's work was well known. What is of interest is his prescience in anticipating some naval activities of World War II. He said that such a vessel might enter any harbour without being suspected, and place any amount of explosive matter under the bottoms of ships at anchor, thus rendering even iron and iron-clad ships unsafe when blockading a port.

Other glimpses of the marriage come from his correspondence with Helen D'Arcy Stewart, of Kinneil House, by Bo'ness, with whom he stayed when a candidate for the Chair of Mathematics at Edinburgh University. She was the wife of Dugald Stewart, former Professor of Moral Philosophy at Edinburgh, friend of Scott, sympathizer with the French Revolution, and tutor of Palmerston, Russell and Lansdowne.

To the superstitious there is something ominous in a letter to Mrs. Stewart from Torquay, dated 22nd September 1819. Charles said that his wife and eldest boy were in good health, and the child was highly delighted with the peacock feathers, but 'Mamma insisted on two of them being put by until the young philosopher can appreciate the value which the donor's name confers upon them'.

Mrs. Stewart replied on 4th December:

'You make me vain of the admiration the peacock feathers met with, and I assure you when we are walking in the avenue and the pea fowls following us, we often begin to talk of you, without remembering why, and always end with wishing that you and all your family were fairly settled in Edinburgh.'

On 6th January 1820 she sent her sincere congratulations on Mrs. Babbage's recovery from the birth of her third boy, to be named Edward Stewart Babbage, after Edward Bromhead and Dugald Stewart. Mrs. Stewart said that her husband felt most flattered, but lamented that his little godson should not receive a prettier name from him, but thought Edward made amends for that. She begged a description of the little boy and hoped that Mrs. Babbage would send her a lock of his hair. She concluded: 'With best respects to Mrs. Babbage and best wishes to all your Pets.'

In April 1821 Charles introduced his young family by name.

'First I will speak of little Stewart whom you mention so kindly, he is the finest and largest of them all. Although he is fifteen months old he does not walk yet, not from any want of ability but from having a decided opinion that locomotion is much more safely performed by crawling on the carpet at which he is very expert. My eldest boy is named Benjamin Herschel after my father and one of my earliest and most intimate friends. The second, Charles Whitmore, has his mother's name, and my little Georgiana with her Mother's name promises to have her Mother's excellence. I shall find it very difficult not to spoil her. I do not observe that my children are more clever than others of their age, nor should I rejoice if they were so at their period of life. I endeavour to give them habits of observing everything that passes before their eyes and in my elder ones I am very contented with their progress.'

In May 1821 he was writing to Mrs. Stewart about a protégé of hers, whom he had invited to live with them. Georgiana's views were not mentioned. 'Our establishment is small, consisting of two female servants, we keep very little company and live in a very plain, quiet, regular way. If Mr. Wedderburn should be our guest we shall consider him quite as one of the family. He will have a sitting-room to which he can retire whenever he wishes and pursue his studies, and my library will always be at his service.'

To this Mrs. Stewart replied that she was really overwhelmed by Mr. Babbage's goodness—who but he would have thought of such a proposal—it was more like the hospitality and kindness of the Golden Age than of anything that ever happened in London.

'And', she continued, not hesitating to emphasize Georgiana's part in it, 'Mrs. Babbage's *goodness* in allowing such a proposal astonishes me so much. With your lovely family, to think of being plagued with a stranger is a proof of generous and kind feelings beyond expression. May your beloved children meet with as kind friends in their journey through life as you are to those you generously think need assistance.'

In the event Charles was unable to fulfil his promise, for he wrote eventually to Mrs. Stewart and Sir David Wedderburn suggesting that the boy should postpone his visit as he (Charles) had received a pressing invitation from Sir William and Lady Herschel to accompany their son John to Switzerland. Georgiana was perhaps not disappointed.

But little Stewart who was so slow to walk was to die a few months after his proud papa's description of him as 'the finest and largest of them all'.

On 26th December 1821 Mrs. Stewart wrote that she was certain no friends they had could sympathize more truly with him and Mrs. Babbage than she and her husband did. The loss of their 'Dear Infant' seemed to them a personal distress, he was a pleasing memorial of their regard, and one in whose happiness they must always have taken a deep interest. He was now safe from sorrow and eternally happy—but his parents *must* feel the blow. God grant their future lives might be left with the health and prosperity of their remaining family.

Papa, too, was ill, from too many hours spent in his library and workshop. Mrs. Stewart added:

'Above all, may you, my dear Sir, soon be restored to perfect health and to all your old and favourite pursuits. From having so often seen literary men bring on by over study disorders that forced them to give up work entirely for some time, it never startles me though much it grieves me, well knowing the severe trial it is. At your age, care and obedience to your Physicians will soon get the better of any complaint.'

Other glimpses of Charles's married life come from Edward Bromhead. With characteristic wit and charm the latter wrote soon after Stewart's birth in 1819:

'I beg to offer yourself and Mrs. Babbage my best congratulations: Edward Stewart Babbage will on the whole have a very Royal sound and I need not say that I feel honoured by having my name associated with that of Dugald Stewart, and I would protest on behalf of this promising youth against the incumbrance of four names, and indeed there is a dreadful want of euphony about Bromhead Babbage. No young lady could fall in love with such Dutch denomination and some future Byron might exclaim,

' "Phoebus, what a name." '

But later he was writing to express his own and his parents' sympathy on the death of this 'promising youth'. He said: 'Poor Mrs. Babbage must have required all your power of consolation.'

Seven months later, on 20th August 1822, he was condoling again:

'After the very melancholy letters which I have lately received from you, I feel a painful hesitation in writing to enquire after the health of yourself and Mrs. Babbage and the rest of the family. If an increasing family brings much pleasure to Parents there is an actual certainty of occasionally suffering from the numerous casualties of tender years. I sincerely wish you happy.'

While Georgiana lived there was no end to the confinements. Bromhead's next letter was to congratulate them upon 'the addition to your store of comforts against old age'.

At this distance of time, and in this day and age, it is impossible not to sympathize with Charles's charming young wife, and to ask why he so consistently ignored her. That he did so is certain. Mrs. Dugald Stewart implied it. Captain F. W.

Marryat said it, and on 8th February 1820 explained the reason why:

'I belong to so many erudite societies that I shall soon have the whole alphabet at my heels, as however I like the idea of yours [the Royal Astronomical Society] I beg you will inscribe Capt. Marryat, R.N., F.R.S., F.L.S., F.G.S., F.W.S., &c. among the members, leaving out by the bye all the letters I have annexed to my name or they will think me some new comet by the length of my tail. You might as well have let me [know] how your wife was, while you were about it, but I of course know that when science is on the tapis all other information is secondary. I shall be up in town in a fortnight and will come to ask myself.'

Perhaps Georgiana, surveying her brood, wryly consoled herself with the reflection that while she may have been ignored, she was most certainly not neglected.

5

Sir Alphabet Function

*

*H*AVING rejected banking and opted for science, Charles Babbage was entirely dependent on his father. While indulging in scientific pursuits, he had hoped, as he relates in his autobiography, to derive from them some benefits for his family or, at least, partly to recoup himself for the expenditure on one of his 'most important discoveries'. His failure on two occasions to obtain an academic post was, however, infinitely more of a blow to his pride than his pocket.

When early in 1816 the Professorship of Mathematics at the East India College at Haileybury became vacant, he applied for it, the salary, he recollected in old age, being about £500 a year. Armed with strong recommendations, he was told that it was customary for candidates to call on the directors. 'One of them', he says, 'was an honest man, for he was kind enough to tell me the truth. He said: "If you have interest, you will get it. If not, you will not succeed." '

The same thing occurred when three years later he applied for the Chair of Mathematics at the University of Edinburgh. On this occasion he had a particularly glittering array of recommendations; Sir William Herschel; J. F. W. Herschel; Peter Mark Roget; Professor Leslie; W. Whewell; J. Pond, F.R.S., Astronomer Royal; Dr. Hutton; Sir Joseph Banks; Richard Gwatkin, Fellow of St. John's College, Cambridge, Senior Moderator of the University; George Peacock, Fellow of Trinity College and Junior Moderator; Dr. Isaac Milner, Dean of Carlisle, President of Queen's and Lucasian Professor of Mathematics; Davies Gilbert, Commissioner, Board of Longitude; and three of Charles's most admired Frenchmen, MM. Biot and Lacroix, and the Marquis Laplace.

On 27th July 1819 John Herschel, after expressing his admiration for his friend's 'originality of inventive genius' and the 'blameless tenor' of his private life, said: 'My father begs you to be assured of his best wishes for your success, which he knows as well as I do is yours if merit will secure it. He would have told you so himself, but for some difficulty he now experiences in the act of writing.' Three days later Edward Bromhead wrote from Thurlby House, Newark, suggesting people to 'wait on' in Edinburgh, adding that *his* father, Sir Gonville, believed that if Charles failed it would be because he was not a 'Scotchman'.

These doubts, based on knowledge of the world, expressed by Sir William Herschel and Sir Gonville Bromhead were fully justified. Edward Bromhead, on 27th October 1819, wrote again: 'I have received your letter and, as I expected, those rascally Scotchmen wheedled you out of your just claims. I hate the Scotch.'

These experiences made a profound impression on Charles Babbage. Conscious as he undoubtedly was, and must inevitably have been, of his own genius, he was now also aware of the fact that compared with interest and patronage even transcendent genius was nothing. The knowledge rankled. It impelled him to write some unfinished and hitherto unpublished lines entitled 'Sir Alphabet Function'. They are witty and amusing and they reveal for the first time the strong vein of cynicism that was to become so marked a feature of his character in later years. They describe how

'Sir Alphabet Function, a knight much renowned,
Who had gained little credit on classical ground,
Set out through the world his fortune to try,
With nought in his pate but his x, v and y.'

At India House Sir Alphabet is interviewed by Chairman Crafty, who promises him the vacant Chair of 'high degree', only to break his promise later on. Then, says the disillusioned poet:

> 'Gay by the brilliant touch of fancy,
> Enhanced by hope's false necromancy,
> With joys that earthly fate might never
> For one blessed state from millions sever
> Would anticipated station be,
> Succeeding visions mocking as they flee
> And all alike remote from cold reality.
> Such the bright dreams of hope for ever new
> For ever cheating, for ever true.
> Experience vainly schools th' enthusiast mind,
> Facts weigh but light 'gainst sophistry refined,
> Unreal schemes in fleet succession rise
> As soapsud bubbles speed them to the skies.
> These by light hydrogen upraised to heaven
> Those by the vanity of Function driven,
> Empty, though smooth, by fortune curst
> Alike they rise, they glitter and they burst.'

Even when in 1824 he was offered lucrative and congenial employment it came to nothing, but for a different reason. He was asked to organize and later to manage a life-insurance office. After making a preliminary investigation of the then existing life-assurance tables and of a published paper of the Actuary of the Equitable Assurance Office, he was able to construct a table of the actual mortality in society. On this basis he calculated the tables for the proposed institution, but establishment of the latter, owing to the absence of reliable data, proved impracticable.

Up to this time almost all life premiums had been constructed from tables prepared by Dr. Price from observations at Northampton. These, as Charles Babbage showed, were calculated from insufficient data. He pointed out—to the annoyance of the existing assurance offices and other vested interests —that the value of the expectation of life must necessarily be affected in varying degrees among different classes of society, by their different social habits as well as by their difference of clothing, food, habitation, locality and other variables.

The vast amount of information and experience gained was not, however, wasted. Charles Babbage concluded that the public was not sufficiently informed about the nature of assurance on lives, and was to publish, in 1826, a small popular work on the subject, which created great interest in his own country and was in the following year translated into German and published in Weimar, becoming the basis upon which the great Life Assurance Society of Gotha was founded.

He kept two letters on the subject, both of which to a later generation have their lighter side.

An inebriated barrister wrote to him from Hereford on 4th August 1823: 'What are the odds that a man of fair health of 32 years of age lives one year? Pray answer the above question to settle a bet and direct it to me on the Oxford circuit.' A clergyman, writing from Nottingham on 1st June 1827, explained that he wished to start a provident society for 'the wasteful lower classes' and asked Charles if he could advise him on the percentage of annuities.

Thus, in spite of the recurring cycle of procreation, birth and death, and the inability to earn a livelihood, life at 5 Devonshire Street, whatever Georgiana may have thought of it, was full of fascination for Charles. Experiments were unceasingly conducted in the workshop above the coach house. He had been elected a Fellow of the Royal Society. Many papers on abstruse mathematical problems were contributed to the *Philosophical Transactions of the Royal Society*, the *Journal of the Royal Institution*, the *Edinburgh Philosophical Journal*, the *Transactions of the Royal Society of Edinburgh* and the *Transactions of the Cambridge Philosophical Society*. Among these was an account of Euler's method of solving a problem relating to the knight's move at chess; another was the examination of some questions connected with games of chance.

Charles was still an 'easy touch', but now brought more critical analysis to bear than when at Cambridge. But he still could not believe that every beggar was a fraud, so, finding it difficult to select 'the few objects on whom I could bestow my very moderate means of charity', he made his own personal investigation.

This was disappointing. He found, firstly, that no matter in which part of London he might happen to be, the beggar's domicile was invariably as far away as possible; secondly, that those who professed to want work and not charity 'always belonged to trades in which it was scarcely possible to give them employment without trusting them with valuable property'. Nevertheless, throughout his life many sixpences continued surreptitiously to change hands.

During those early years of his married life he paid his first visit to Paris, accompanied by John Herschel, and at Abbeville caused no little sensation by ordering two boiled eggs for each of them—'*pour chacun deux*'. The waiter misunderstood his English accent and shouted: '*Il faut faire bouillir cinquante-deux œufs pour Messieurs les Anglais.*' Charles burst into such a fit of uncontrollable laughter that he was unable to move, but Herschel, realizing what had happened, ran into the kitchen and countermanded the order for 'the half-hundred of eggs'.

The story, with embellishments, preceded them to Paris. They were dining with Laplace and members of the Institut when one of the latter remarked to Charles that two young Englishmen had ordered fifty-two eggs for breakfast and had eaten every one in addition to a large pie. Another asked him whether he thought it probable. Charles, tongue in cheek, replied that there was no absurdity a young Englishman would not occasionally commit.

On this visit he met not only Laplace but also Poisson, Fourier and Biot, who became his intimate friends. Fourier, who was then secretary of the Institut, had accompanied the first Napoleon on his expedition to Egypt; Biot's son, an orientalist, was to translate *The Economy of Manufactures*, and when beards became fashionable among 'a certain class' of Englishman, Biot, looking Charles straight in the face, said: 'My dear friend, you are the best-shaved man in Europe.' Thus he became acquainted with some of the greatest, and his own most admired, figures in the science of numerical analysis.

Another important event was the foundation of the Royal

Astronomical Society by Dr. Pearson, F.R.S., whose most active and energetic supporter was Charles Babbage. A meeting was held on 12th January 1820, to draw up the rules, the committee consisting of Charles himself, Francis Baily, F.R.S., Captain Colby, F.R.S., H. T. Colebrooke, F.R.S., O. Gregory, J. F. W. Herschel, F.R.S., D. Moore, F.R.S., and the Rev. W. Pearson, F.R.S. The first meeting of members was held at the house of the Geological Society in Bedford Place, Covent Garden, on 8th February 1820, Francis Baily acting as secretary, and John Herschel giving an address which was subsequently printed in the first volume of the Society's memoirs.

6

The Philosophers of Laputa

*

SOON after this Charles Babbage was appointed jointly with John Herschel to carry out certain calculations for the Society, the two friends agreeing upon the proper formulae, and then proceeding to engage independent computors to reduce them into numbers.

One day Herschel brought in the computors' calculations, and the two started the tedious process of verification. After a time many discrepancies occurred, and at one point were so numerous that Charles exclaimed: 'I wish to God these calculations had been executed by steam.' Herschel replied: 'It is quite possible.' They continued their tedious comparison without further comment.

During the next few days Charles devoted much thought to the matter, eventually satisfying himself that it was possible to make machinery compute tables by differences, and even to print them when computed. The excitement of the enquiry made him ill and he was advised to abstain for a time from all thought of the 'calculating engine'. Soon, however, he returned to the subject and it began to assume a practicable shape, though still far removed from what it eventually became. 'It was certainly fortunate for me', he said, 'both at this period, and at many other times, that I had no sufficiently distinct view of the multitude of difficulties, both practical and moral, which were destined to attend its course. If these had not opened upon me by degrees, I might perhaps never have ventured on its execution.'

He made a small model, containing three figure wheels on

the table axis, two on that of the first difference and one on the second difference. He was still, however, very far from being aware of the almost insuperable difficulties which such a subject would present to any mind not familiar with both the mathematical and mechanical difficulties involved; and being in some degree afraid that his invention might be forestalled, he employed different workmen to execute different parts of the model, finally putting them together with his own hands. This was not without a practical advantage. He failed completely in constructing the first framework, which was of iron and was useless from want of stiffness; another failure convinced him of the importance of the supports as well as of the moving parts; but ultimately a model of six figures worked and gave visible proof of the fact by calculating a few simple tables. He had now accomplished all that his circumstances permitted.

He was just over thirty years old when, on 14th June 1822, he read a paper to the Royal Astronomical Society announcing that he was engaged in the construction of a machine for the purpose of calculating *any* tables that might be required, and was entirely convinced of the success of his undertaking.

'I have taken the method of differences as the principle on which my machinery is founded, and in the engine which is just finished[1] I have limited myself to two orders of differences. With this machine I have repeatedly constructed tables of square and triangular numbers as well as a table from the singular formula $x^2 + x + 41$ which comprises amongst its terms so many prime numbers.'

These, as well as any others which the engine was competent to form, were produced almost as rapidly as an assistant could write them down, he continued. The machinery was extremely simple, consisting of a small number of different parts frequently repeated.

In carrying out this plan he had contrived methods by which type should be set up by the machine, in the order determined by the calculation, and the arrangements were of such a nature that if executed there should not exist the possibility of error in any printed copy of tables computed by the engine. Of several

1. He meant, of course, the model.

of these latter contrivances he had made various models and from experiments already conducted he felt great confidence in their complete success.

In these glowing tones he announced one of the most revolutionary schemes ever to be devised by any human being. For while machines had long existed which enabled one man to perform the physical labour of many, Charles Babbage's invention substituted mechanical performance for an intellectual process.

He amplified these details on 3rd July 1822, in a letter to Sir Humphry Davy, Bart., President of the Royal Society, remarking that the 'intolerable labour and fatiguing monotony' of a continued repetition of similar mathematical calculations had first excited his desire and afterwards suggested the idea of a machine which 'by the aid of gravity or any other moving power' should become a substitute for one of the 'lowest occupations of the human intellect'.

The first engine of which drawings were made was capable of computing any table by the aid of differences, whether they were positive or negative, or both. In his own opinion, and in that of a 'skilful mechanic' whom he had consulted, the number of the order of differences did not appear to restrict the nature of the machinery to any very limited number, and he would venture to construct a machine with ten or a dozen numbers with perfect confidence. One remarkable property of the machine was that the greater the number of differences the more it would outstrip the most rapid calculators.

By the application of certain parts of no great degree of complexity this could be converted into a machine for extracting the roots of equations and consequently the roots of numbers, the extent of the approximation depending on the magnitude of the machine. Of a machine for multiplying any number of figures (m) by any other number (n) he had several sketches, but was not at the stage where he would wish to see it carried out. He had, too, certain principles by which, if it should be desirable, a table of prime numbers might be made, extending from 0 to 10,000,000.

Another machine, whose plans were much more advanced

than several of those just named, was one for constructing tables which had no order of constant differences. A great variety of equations of finite differences might by its means be solved, and a variety of tables, which could be produced in successive parts by the first machine he had mentioned, could be calculated by the latter with even 'less exertion of human thought'. Another and very remarkable point in the structure of this machine was that it would calculate tables governed by laws which had not been hitherto shown to be explicitly determinable, or that it would solve equations for which analytical methods of solution had not yet been contrived.

But even though these engines fulfilled the inventor's claims there would yet be wanting other means to ensure the accuracy of the printed tables to be produced by them. The errors of those employed to copy the figures presented by the engines would first interfere with their correctness. To remedy this, means had been contrived by which the machines themselves could take from several boxes containing type the numbers which they calculated, and place them side by side, this becoming at the same time a substitute for the compositor and the computor. By this means all error in copying as well as in printing was removed.

There were, however, two other possible sources of error. Each of the ten boxes with which the engine was provided contained about 3,000 types, any box having only those of one number in it. It might happen that the person employed in filling these boxes should accidentally place a wrong type in some of them, as, for example, the number two in the box which ought only to contain sevens. When these boxes were delivered to the superintendent of the machine a simple and efficient means had been provided by which in less than half an hour it could be ascertained whether, among these 3,000 types, any individual type was misplaced or even inverted. The other cause of error arose from the type falling out when the page had been set up. This had been rendered impossible by similar means.

The number of errors from careless proof correcting, even in tables of the greatest credit, could scarcely be believed, he remarked, except by those who had had constant occasion for their use. A friend, whose skill in practical as well as theoretical astronomy was well known, had produced a copy of the tables published by order of the French Board of Longitude, containing those of the sun by Delambre and of the moon by Burg, in which he had corrected over 500 errors, most of which appeared to be printing errors, and it was somewhat remarkable that on the fourth page which he, Charles Babbage himself, had opened he observed a new error, hitherto unnoticed. These, he emphasized, were so much the more dangerous because independent computors using the same tables would agree in the same errors.

To perfect the various machines would demand an expenditure of time and money that only other inventors could appreciate. He had at present confined himself to sketches on paper, accompanied by short memoranda, and where any new principles were introduced he had had models executed in order to examine their actions. As a practical example, he had chosen the engine for differences, and had constructed one that would produce any tables whose second differences were constant. It was approximately the size he envisaged for a more extensive engine, the chief difference being that in the one intended for use there would be a greater repetition of the same parts in order to adapt it to the calculation of a larger number of figures.

A few trials had been made to show the rapidity with which it could calculate. The first was a table from the formula $x^2 + x + 41$. In the earlier numbers it was possible, writing quickly, to keep up with the engine, but when four figures were required the machine was at least equal in speed to the writer. In a second trial thirty numbers of the same table were calculated in two minutes and thirty seconds. These contained eighty-two figures, so the engine produced thirty-three every minute. In a third trial it produced figures at the rate of forty-four per minute. As the machine could be made to move uniformly by a weight, the rate could be maintained for any length of time. Few writers would be found to copy with equal speed for many hours together.

The parts of which the machine consisted were few but

frequently repeated, resembling in this respect the arithmetic to which it was applied, and which, by the aid of a few digits often repeated, produced all the wide variety of number. The wheels of which it consisted were numerous, but few moved at the same time, and a principle was employed by which any small error that might arise from accident or bad workmanship was corrected as soon as it was produced, thus effectually preventing any accumulation of small errors from producing a wrong figure in the calculation.

If, however, this was still thought incredible, and that there was still the possibility of error, he replied that the method of differences enabled him to determine its existence. Thus, if proper numbers were placed at the outset in the engine, and if it had composed a page of any table, then, by comparing the last number it had set up with the number previously calculated, the whole page must, if they were found to agree, be correct. Should any disagreement occur it would scarcely be worth the trouble of looking for its origin, as it would be quicker to make the engine re-calculate the whole page.

He then described the course pursued in 'one of the most stupendous monuments of arithmetical calculation' which the world had yet produced, stressing the share of mental labour that would have been saved by employing such an engine as he had contrived. The tables concerned were those calculated under the direction of M. Prony, by order of the French Government, and they occupied seventeen large folio volumes, one table alone, that of the logarithms of numbers, containing about 8,000,000 figures.

1. The natural sines of each 10,000th of the quadrant calculated to twenty-five figures with seven or eight orders of differences.

2. The logarithmic sines of each 100,000th of the quadrant calculated to fourteen decimals with five orders of differences.

3. The logarithms of the ratios of the sines to their arcs of the first 5,000 of the 100,000th of the quadrant calculated to fourteen decimals with three orders of differences.

4. The logarithmic tangents corresponding to the logarithmic sines calculated to the same extent.

5. The logarithms of the ratios of the tangents to their arcs, calculated in the same manner as the logarithms of the ratios of the sines to their arcs.

6. The logarithms of numbers, from 1 to 10,000, calculated to nineteen decimals.

7. The logarithms of all numbers from 10,000 to 200,000, calculated to fourteen figures with five orders of differences.

The calculators were divided into three sections, the first comprising five or six mathematicians of the highest merit, including MM. Prony and Legendre. These were occupied entirely with the analytical part of the work, investigating and determining the formulae to be employed. The second section consisted of seven or eight skilful calculators, familiar with both analytical and arithmetical computations. They received the formulae from the first section, converted them into numbers and furnished to the third section the proper differences at the stated intervals. They also received from that section the calculated results, and compared the two sets, which were computed independently for the purpose of verification. The third section, on whom the most laborious part of the operations devolved, consisted of from sixty to eighty persons, few of them possessing a knowledge of more than the first rules of arithmetic. These received from the second section certain numbers and differences, with which, by additions and subtractions in a prescribed order, they completed the whole of the above-mentioned tables.

If the difference engine were ever to be employed to complete these or any similar tables of equal extent much labour could be dispensed with. That of the first section would be reduced because the formulae used had already been investigated and published. One person, or at the utmost two, might therefore conduct it. If the second section, instead of delivering their calculations to the computors of the third section, were to deliver them to the engine, all the remaining operations would be executed by machinery, and it would only be necessary to employ people to copy down as fast as they were able the figures presented to them by the engine. If, however, the printing mechanism were perfected, even this labour would be unnecessary, and a few superintendents could manage the machine and receive the calculated pages set up in type. Thus the number of calculators employed, instead of approaching ninety-six, would be reduced to twelve. And this number, too, might be diminished, because when an engine was used the intervals between the differences calculated by the second section could be greatly enlarged.

He felt justified in assuming that if engines were made purposely for this object, and were afterwards useless, the tables could be produced at a much cheaper rate, and of their superior accuracy there could be no doubt. They would, however, be far from useless, containing within themselves the power of generating to an almost unlimited extent tables whose accuracy would be unrivalled, at comparatively moderate expense. They would also become active agents in reducing the abstract enquiries of geometry to a form and an arrangement adapted to the ordinary purposes of human society, while almost all astronomical tables for determining the positions of the sun or planets were also capable of being calculated by the methods of differences.

He was aware that his claims might perhaps be regarded as Utopian, and that the philosophers of Laputa might be called up to dispute his claim to originality. Conscious, from his own experience, of the difficulty of convincing those who were but little skilled in mathematical knowledge, of making a machine to perform calculations, he was anxious, in introducing it to the public, to appeal to the testimony of so distinguished a scientist as Sir Humphry Davy. Of the extent to which the machinery might be carried, opinions would naturally fluctuate until experiment finally decided their relative value, but of the engine which already existed he believed he would be supported by Sir Humphry Davy and other scientists who had examined it. What happened would depend on the nature of the encouragement he might receive, for such an undertaking could be attained only with considerable expense over a long period of time. And, he might have added, in spite of the opposition of the philosophers of Laputa.

7

No Treasury Minute

*

*H*IS next step was to submit to the Government a plan for 'applying machinery to the purpose of calculating and printing mathematical tables'. On 1st April 1823 the Lords of the Treasury, through their Secretary, requested the Royal Society to take the plan into consideration, their Lordships further desiring 'to be favoured with the opinion of the Royal Society on the merits and utility of this invention'.

The council of the Royal Society in turn referred the matter to a committee, consisting of Sir Humphry Davy, Mr. Brande, Mr. Combe, Mr. Francis Baily, Mr. (afterwards Sir) Mark Isambard Brunel, Major Colby, Mr. Davies Gilbert, J. F. W. Herschel, Captain Kater, J. Pond (Astronomer Royal), Dr. Wollaston and Dr. Thomas Young.

Dr. Young's was the only dissentient voice. He, without doubting that a calculating machine could be made, believed that it would be better to invest the probable cost of such a machine and apply the dividends to paying human calculators.

He, however, was in a minority of one, and on 1st May the Committee reported:

'It appears that Mr. Babbage has displayed great talents and ingenuity in the construction of his machine for computation which the Committee think fully adequate to the attainment of the objects proposed by the inventor, and that they consider Mr. Babbage as highly deserving of public encouragement in the prosecution of his arduous undertaking.'

This report, together with Charles Babbage's letter to Sir

Humphry Davy, was subsequently printed and laid before Parliament.

In the following July Charles had an interview with the Chancellor of the Exchequer, F. J. Robinson, later Viscount Goderich and later still first Earl of Ripon. In view of subsequent events it was tragic that no minute or written record of this conversation was made at the time, nor was any sufficiently distinct understanding arrived at between the parties. This was to bedevil the whole undertaking and to prove the main source of trouble to the end. The conviction in the mind of Charles Babbage was, however, that whatever might be the labour and difficulty of the undertaking, the engine itself would become the property of the Government which had paid for its construction.

The Chancellor, according to Charles's recollection, remarked that the Government were in general unwilling to make grants of money for any inventions, however meritorious, because if the inventions really possessed the merit claimed for them the sale of the article produced would be the inventor's best, as well as his largest, reward. But, he added, the present case was an exception, since it was obvious that the construction of such a machine could not be undertaken with a view to profit from the sale of its produce; and that as mathematical tables were peculiarly valuable for nautical purposes, it was considered a fit object of encouragement by the Government.

Two methods of advancing money for the construction were mentioned: either through the recommendation of a committee of the House of Commons, or by taking a sum from the civil contingencies; and the Chancellor observed that as the session of Parliament was nearing its end, the latter course might perhaps be the most convenient. Charles Babbage thought that the Chancellor also made some observation indicating that the amount of money taken from the civil contingencies would be smaller than that which might be obtained by means of a committee of the House of Commons, and that he proposed to take £1,000 as a beginning from the civil contingencies fund. Charles enquired whether it would be too much in the first instance to take £1,500. The Chancellor immediately answered that £1,500 should be advanced.

Charles Babbage believed at this time that he would be able to complete the engine in two, or, at the most, in three, years, and that by having £1,500 in the first instance he would be able to advance, from his own private funds, the residue of the £3,000, or even £5,000, which he then imagined the engine might possibly cost, so that he would not again have occasion to apply to Government until it was completed. Some observations were made by the Chancellor about the mode of accounting for the money received, as well as about its expenditure, but it seemed to be admitted that it was not possible to prescribe any very definite means for carrying out the plan, and that much must be left to the inventor's own judgement.

Soon after this interview the Royal Society was informed by the Treasury that they 'had directed the issue of £1,500 to Mr. Babbage, to enable him to bring his invention to perfection in the manner recommended'. Buxton suggests that the words 'in the manner recommended' must necessarily have referred to some previous recommendation by the Royal Society, but it did not appear from their report that any plan, terms or conditions had been pointed out by that body, or that any had been imposed upon the inventor.

Charles now embarked on the actual construction of the machine. At once his earlier misgivings were multiplied a hundredfold. He realized that in his zeal and enthusiasm he had gravely underestimated the practical and mechanical difficulties. After years of bitter experience he was to say that while an inventor might not be far from the truth in having imagined an instrument possessing the most remarkable powers of calculation, he would be very remote from the attainment of its execution and probably spend months or years or even life itself in vainly attempting to surmount the difficulties of some few of its successive stages.

Henry Thomas Colebrooke, F.R.S., in presenting him with the Gold Medal of the Royal Astronomical Society on 13th July 1823, gave some indication of this, if only by inference. It was, in scope as in execution, he said, unlike anything before accomplished to assist laborious computations. He passed by, as obviously quite different, the Shivanpan, or Chinese abacus,

75

the tangible arithmetic of Frend, Napier's rods, with the rude devices of antiquity, the tallies, the check and the counters. They were unconnected with it in purpose as in form. Mechanical aids had, of course, been proposed by very eminent persons. Pascal had invented a very complicated instrument for the simplest arithmetical processes, addition and subtraction, and reaching by very tedious repetition to multiplication and division. Leibniz proposed another, of which the power extended no farther. Delepine's and Boitissendeau's contrivances, which had been applauded by the Paris Academy of Sciences a century before, were based on the model of Pascal's, and were no doubt improvements of it, but did not vary or enlarge its objects. The principle which essentially distinguished Charles Babbage's invention from all these was that it proposed to calculate a series of numbers following any law by the aid of differences, and that by setting a few figures at the outset a long series of numbers was readily produced by a mechanical operation.

For these reasons adduced by Colebrooke, the machinery which Charles Babbage contemplated was necessarily so complex that a thousand obstacles lay in his path. These, he now found, could be overcome only by his own ingenuity and individual resources. No one could help him. He had, in fact, embarked upon a new career, for, apart from the limited experience gained through making models, he had no knowledge of engineering, of tool-making or of metal-working. He ought to have had the unlimited resources of Government workshops, and to have been relieved of the burden of checking accounts and worrying about the workmen.

Instead, he had to examine for himself, as far as he was able, the resources of the existing workshops, soon arriving at the conclusion that he would have to invent many of the tools himself. Joseph Clement, who became one of the foremost tool-makers of the day, was put in charge of operations, under his direction. Workmen of the highest skill were constantly employed in making the tools, and afterwards in using them for the construction of various parts of the machine.

As time passed, the knowledge acquired by these workmen was gradually improved and infiltrated into other workshops. Many of the most enlightened employers and constructors of machines, who had themselves contributed to its advancement, told Charles Babbage in later years that even if his calculating machine had proved a failure, still the money expended by the Government in his attempt to make it would have been most beneficially invested and would be found to have been well and amply repaid by the advancement in mechanical construction. This proved poor consolation for the inventor.

Another grave difficulty was the utter impossibility of remembering all the variety of motions brought simultaneously into action. Obviously, nothing but the most complete harmony and precise order among such a system of movements could avoid an obstruction among the parts, and he soon found the need for some aid to the memory, as well as the ability to see what every moving piece of machinery was doing at each instant of time. This formidable obstacle, which might have tried the courage or baffled the ingenuity of most men, proved only an incentive to further effort on his part, for he realized that unless he could devise some means of adequate pre-vision he would have to abandon the scheme altogether.

'I soon felt that the forms of ordinary language are far too diffuse to admit of any expectation of removing the difficulty, and being convinced from experience of the vast power which analysis derives from the great condensation of meaning in the language it employs, I was not long in deciding that the most favourable path to pursue was to have recourse to the language of signs.'

This system he called the mechanical notation, and it was applicable to all machinery. It consisted of an arrangement of signs which enabled him, by directing his eye along a line, to trace the motion of every piece of the machine, from effect to cause. The signs included the Arabic and Roman alphabets, capital letters, lower-case letters, letters in italics and dotted and broken lines, as well as figures in different positions. Motion was depicted by an arrow, and different kinds of motion by variations in the arrow.

Years later, in 1841, he was able to sum up, in comparatively few words, what he went through during those early days. They fail, nevertheless, to convey the degree of mental turmoil, the anguish, the nervous tension, the disappointment and the frustration which he suffered.

After forming a general conception of the machine, he said, it was necessary to divide it into a multitude of simpler elements, and to contrive fitting mechanism to execute each, and to ensure the means by which these might be made to act in unison. The parts by which each portion of the several operations was accomplished must then be again subdivided. Addition, for instance, would consist of a combination of mechanism for adding the digits, and another portion must be contrived for carrying the tens. It was obvious that special contrivances must be invented for each of these operations. These tentative contrivances might be sketched at first roughly, and it would probably happen that many of them would be thrown aside before they were finished, and many more would be rejected after completion, as failing to insure the object of their construction. From time to time different principles would suggest themselves, and after much meditation one plan would be sketched more in detail and finally become the basis upon which the mechanism would be completed and drawn in its proper magnitude and proportion, together with the necessary details for its execution. In the course of this process it was necessary to devise framework by which each part might be properly supported; and when the inventor had arrived at this stage of his progress he should resort to the employment of scale and compass, so as to secure accuracy in the relative magnitude of each portion, and the requisite strength on the one hand, and convenient lightness of the moving parts on the other. The neglect of these precautions was a frequent source of failure in the working of machinery otherwise excellent, and amateurs were especially liable to difficulties arising from an inattention to these precepts.

In order to be thoroughly master of the machine, it was desirable at this stage to examine how each piece of metal, whether wheel, lever or other part, might be formed by the workmen, and in cases of peculiar difficulty, or where a multitude of similar parts was required, to contrive tools for their execution.

If the inventor had succeeded in passing through the former stages without employment of the mechanical notation, or some equivalent method of representing the times of the action of each piece, much time and labour had probably been wasted, and it would now become absolutely impossible to dispense with it any longer.

The mechanical drawings merely gave a picture of the position of the parts at one moment of time. All the successive motions of each part must now be represented in that language which could command the power of communicating to the eye, and almost at a glance, either the successive course of each movement or the contemporaneous effect of many, and at the same time mask all such movements as were not absolutely required for the parts under investigation.

It was then necessary to arrange the general combination of the whole engine, and decide on the relative position of the several groups. Connections would also have to be planned and drawn, and framing devised to support the whole. Many mechanical notations of various kinds would be found necessary for this work, and other notations made to represent the movements of the engine as a whole. Besides these, a series of notations had to be made of the various combinations of operations which the machine had to perform.

When this had been attained the invention of the machine could be regarded as complete. The drawings would have demonstrated the possibility of the existence of the machine in space, and of the power of its framework to support all its parts; whilst the mechanical notation would fully prove that the machine possessed the requisite powers of movement, and that no incompatibility existed between the various motions.

The checks which these notations perpetually supplied rendered it impossible to advance many steps without detecting existing errors, which might have in the first instance escaped observation. It might easily be supposed that all these several steps in the invention of machinery were very rarely pursued, with all the necessary precision; the several stages of invention were in practice usually more or less mixed up with one another, and, indeed, the occasional change of direction which the mind received from various associations, when it turned from the consideration of minute parts, and passed from special contrivances to general combinations, was rather favourable to discovery than otherwise.

When the inventor was thus far advanced, the remaining stages related to the actual execution of the machine. His efforts should now be met with less difficulty, yet it was not to expected that all obstacles had been entirely overcome. He was now stepping into a new field of exertion, and in order to command success he must be prepared to exert a degree of skill differing from that which had guided him to the present point of his labours. Separate drawings must be made of each individual piece of the machine, and of many of their partial combinations. He should not be appalled by this necessary accumulation of labour, for the work was not difficult in itself, and, though extensive, many individuals might be employed and the labour distributed.

The last stage of the inventor's labours was the making of the individual parts and putting the whole together. Considerable skill was required in supplying the workshop with the necessary tools, of which such a number should be provided that no workman should be delayed for want of the necessary aids to labour, or for the want of parts of machinery remaining unexecuted. The working drawings should first be put into the hands of the pattern-maker, and the pattern then sent to the foundry, and when the castings were executed the pattern should be returned.

It was then that the workmen received the drawings and the castings, and proceeded to form the latter into their destined plan, either in the lathe, the planing, or the drilling machines, or by means of the special tools contrived for their respective purposes. As the adjacent parts were successively executed they were to be tried with one another, and ultimately the whole put together.

One of the most frequent sources of difficulty arose from commencing the two last stages prematurely, and before the

Charles Babbage, aged thirty-six. From a Colnaghi engraving

Mrs. Charles Babbage, *née* Georgiana Whitmore. From a miniature in the possession of Mrs. M. A. Phillips

Major-General Henry Provost Babbage, aged seventy

drawings and notations were completely finished. Another source of embarrassment was occasioned by permitting any change in the design after the workmen had started. The difficulties and delays occasioned by an alteration apparently trifling could be appreciated only by those who had practical experience.

A major issue which Babbage entirely omitted to mention was that much of the cost of the difference engine was swallowed up in preliminary experimentation; for no step was taken without the preparation of a drawing, and, as each drawing was made, a new enquiry was held to determine the mechanical means by which the several parts were to be formed, thus necessitating further drawings for the purpose of constructing the tools. This was followed by further experimentation or trial, when some simpler mode of construction would perhaps be suggested, and so, from time to time, the original contrivances were superseded, modified or improved.

Superseded, modified, improved . . . These words must have been engraved on Charles Babbage's heart.

8

'The Thing is a Humbug'

*

*I*N 1827, and while in the middle of all these difficulties, he was overwhelmed by a series of personal tragedies and became very ill.

'I lost my father, my wife and two children. My family, acting on the advice of my medical friends, urged me to travel abroad for six or twelve months. It was thought necessary that I should be accompanied by a servant in case of illness or accident. I objected to this on the ground that I was but just able to take care of myself, and that a servant would (to me) be a great encumbrance. To satisfy, however, a mother's anxiety I proposed to take with me one of my own workmen if he liked to accompany me as an attendant.'

The man, named Richard Wright, agreed to accompany his master, who described him as 'a faithful friend of mine'.

In these words, written on 16th January 1871, when Charles Babbage was within a few months of his own death, he described a series of events from which, in a sense, he never recovered. What was worse, they occurred at a time when he was overwrought by the difficulties of constructing the difference engine. According to his own calculations it should have been finished by now; but in some ways it was as far as ever from completion, and ugly rumours were beginning to circulate, culminating with 'Professor Airy says the thing is a humbug. Other scientific men say the contrary.'

William Macready, the actor, was not to make this entry in his diary for another ten years, but the sentiment expressed was well in evidence in 1827. And if people of George Biddell Airy's eminence could say it then it was inevitable that a seed of suspicion should be sown in the minds of people who knew nothing of science or of Charles Babbage; for Airy's qualifications paralleled Charles's, and from a worldly point of view were more dazzling: senior wrangler and first Smith's prizeman, 1823; fellow of Trinity College, Cambridge, 1824; Lucasian Professor of Mathematics, 1826; Plumian Professor of Astronomy and director of Cambridge Observatory, 1828; Astronomer Royal, 1835–81.

Only one conclusion could be drawn from such statements as Airy's—the inventor was wasting public money. The conclusion was already being drawn in 1827, regardless of the possibility that Airy, who loved doing arithmetic, and others might be of Luddite mentality, resenting the idea of any part of their work being performed by a machine.

This tragic combination of circumstances plunged Charles Babbage into a nervous breakdown. He first stopped work in August 1827 in order to take Georgiana, who was again pregnant, to Boughton, an estate on the outskirts of Worcester, the home of her sister Harriet and brother-in-law J. Isaac, banker of Worcester.

The situation derives additional poignancy from being seen through the eyes of a little child. Henry Babbage was only three years old at the time, and his first recollection was of being in the care of a Mrs. Powell, wife of his uncle's bailiff, who lived in the lodge at the entrance gate. His parents travelled from London on 4th August 1827, and there, in September, Georgiana died, after giving birth to another boy.

'One of my earliest recollections is the mourning dress for my mother,' he said, 'which hurt me in wearing, and I did not like it in consequence and cried when it was put on; probably I was considered a sensitive child.'

He apparently had no recollection of his father at this time. With his elder brother Dugald he was left for a year or two in the care of the Powells, whom they called 'Daddy' and 'Mammy'. Mrs. Powell was very kind to them and Henry never forgot her. The two children played about the fields and when it was time for a meal Mrs. Powell summoned them by banging a shovel with a poker. They were sent to a small school near the lodge, but spent much of their time at the big house, where they were great favourites of their cousins, the Isaac and Ryan children. In the meantime the two elder Babbage children, Herscher and Georgiana, were at 5 Devonshire Street in the care of their grandmother, who was now inevitably drawn closer than ever to her son.

Charles was now thirty-six and, by the terms of his father's will, a rich man. Benjamin Babbage, whose will was made in June 1826 and proved in London on 26th February 1827, left to his son all his plate, library, land and (with certain exceptions) property, and afterwards to Charles's children, the value being £100,000. To his wife he left £21,000, £10,000 of it on trust for Charles's five eldest children on attaining their majority, otherwise in trust for them; his property in East Teignmouth, and the use of a diamond necklace, crescent ring, pin and locket for her life, afterwards to Charles for his 'absolute use'.

So Charles could now do as he pleased and go where he wished. But, as so often happens, it had come too late. There was no one to share it with, there was no Georgiana to wear the diamond ornaments when his mother had finished with them. It was as though he locked up the memory of his wife in a secret compartment of his heart, making a vow never to mention her again, except (and it was then probably quite involuntarily) on his own death-bed over forty years hence. And so, utterly bereft, in a vain attempt to forget, he set off on his travels.

Just before leaving England another tragedy nearly occurred. He took Herschel, aged twelve, to see the Thames Tunnel, between Wapping and Rotherhithe, then in process of construction. The younger Brunel took them into the workings, and they were standing together talking when a commotion occurred some distance away. Suddenly Charles noted a considerable stream of liquid mud issuing from an upper corner. Brunel at once formed a line of workmen, who, armed with suitable tools, managed to stop the incoming flow, explaining that unless he or Gravett, another engineer, had been present the tunnel would have been flooded in less than ten minutes. A week later, by this time on the Continent, Charles read in Galignani's newspaper that another inundation had occurred in which five or six workmen were drowned and Brunel had only escaped with difficulty by swimming.

Part Two
(1827–1842)

*

Seldom comes Glory till a man be dead.
ROBERT HERRICK, *Hesperides*, No. 624

9

Grand Tour

*

CHARLES BABBAGE started his grand tour by crossing to Holland and going on to Germany. Judging by the careful preparations which he made and some of the contents of his luggage, expressly designed to curry favour with the natives, he might have been going to explore some of the more remote regions of darkest Africa instead of Europe.

Among his 'trade goods' were half a dozen copies in French, and half a dozen in German, of an account of the Thames Tunnel, and, surprisingly enough, they were gratefully received for services rendered. Other merchandise consisted of two dozen gold buttons stamped by steel dies, which had the property of becoming iridescent in the sunlight, an effect achieved by ruling the steel die in parallel lines up to one ten-thousandth of an inch apart. He carried a die in his writing-case and in a waistcoat pocket a small piece of steel ruled in the same way, together with a gold button in a sandalwood case. These were to prove very useful. 'The mere sight of them procured me many little attentions in diligences and steamboats.'

In Venice he toured a factory where gold chains were made, but wishing to purchase small pieces of them found them much too costly. He therefore whisked out the piece of ruled steel and showed it to the astonished proprietor, who was so impressed that he allowed him to purchase as many short lengths as he wished at a reasonable price.

The stomach pump had just been invented, so he had to go one better and take the parts of an instrument which could be used 'either as a syringe, a stomach pump or for cupping'. As a stomach pump it was in great demand, and at Munich Dr. Weisbrod, the king's physician, asked him to allow the chief surgical-instrument maker to make an exact copy of the whole apparatus.

At Frankfort he met the eldest son of the Czar's coach-maker, who had travelled widely and showed him drawings of the most notable carriages he had ever seen. 'Some of these were selected for their elegance, others for the reverse; take, as an example, the Lord Mayor's.' They travelled together as far as Munich, and with characteristic intellectual curiosity Charles questioned him and made notes. The Russian was on his way to Moscow and begged his companion to accompany him, but Charles, who wished to reach Italy as soon as possible, reluctantly declined the invitation.

He made good use of the information, however, and later on at Vienna had 'a strong, light four-wheeled caleche' built to his own design. It was large enough for him to sleep in at full length. A lamp enabled him to cook his breakfast or boil an egg if he wished. There was a shallow drawer, large enough to take, without folding, 'plans, drawings and dress coats'. Pockets were available for the different kinds of currency and a larger one held books, telescopes and other impedimenta. The calash cost just over £60, and he used it for six months, spending only five francs on repairs and eventually selling it at The Hague for £30.

While in Rome he accidentally read a short item in Galignani, dated Cambridge, saying: 'Yesterday the bells of St. Mary's rang on the election of Mr. Babbage as Lucasian Professor of Mathematics.' This event followed the appointment of Professor Airy to the Plumian Professorship of Astronomy and Directorship of Cambridge Observatory. Although he was to describe it as the only honour which he ever received in his own country, Charles read the announcement with mixed feelings, and even before he received official confirmation had drafted a letter, thanking the University for the honour but declining it. If, he remarked, it had come in his father's lifetime it would have given him all the greater pleasure because of the intense delight given to his mother. What Georgiana would have thought of it he did not say.

Two of his friends, the Rev. Mr. Lunn and Mr. Beilby Thompson, afterwards Lord Wenlock, who were staying in the Piazza del Populo, came to congratulate him and persuaded him to tear up the letter of refusal, stressing firstly that it would give so much pleasure to his mother. To this he made the kind of ungracious reply that so often spoilt him in later life, and caused so many misunderstandings.

'I answered that my mother's opinion of her son had been confirmed by the reception he had met with in every foreign country he had visited, and that this, in her estimation, would add but little to it.'

To this churlishness they patiently replied that the election had been actively promoted not only by some of his own friends but also by others who might have acted entirely on principle, and 'that it would be harsh to disappoint such friends, and reject such a compliment'.

He then reflected that light though the duties of the Lucasian Professor might be, he feared they would take up time which should be given to the difference engine. Urged by his friends, however, he decided to accept the Chair and hold it for a few years. In the event he was to hold it for ten years without giving a single lecture.

While in Rome he had occasion to wear the dress coats which could be accommodated without folding in the shallow drawer of the calash, for there he became acquainted with various members of the Bonaparte family. He was already known to Lucien, Prince of Canino, the eldest brother of Napoleon. Lucien, in exile in England, lived in Worcestershire near the Isaacs, who often visited him. In Rome Charles met Lucien's son, who introduced him to his sisters, Lady Dudley Stuart and the Princess Gabrielli. At Bologna he met another daughter, the Princess d'Ercolano, and renewed acquaintance with her at Florence, 'at the palace of her uncle Louis, the former King of Holland'. In Florence he was presented to the reigning Grand Duke Leopold II, being 'received with a kindness and consideration which I can never forget'.

One of his minor accomplishments was the ability to punch a hole in glass without cracking it, and this enabled him at

Bologna (where he spent several weeks at the University) to put a presumptuous instrument-maker in his place. Wishing to demonstrate his method to a friend, he first politely suggested that the instrument-maker might know the method. The man replied arrogantly: 'Yes, we do it every day.' Observing a look of surprise on the faces of the workmen, Charles thereupon lured him into the position of having to perform the trick, which, of course, he was unable to do, smashing the glass into a hundred fragments.

As a foreign member of the Royal Academy of Naples, he accompanied a commission to report on the hot springs of Ischia, none of which was very deep. In one or two he believed that if bored to a depth of a few feet boiling water would be reached. He then inspected the damage caused by a recent earthquake, which was confined to one small part of the island and hardly felt in others. In some of the streets the houses on one side had collapsed, while the walls of those on the other were standing.

Having missed the earthquake itself, he consoled himself with a 'flirtation with a volcano'. Vesuvius was in a state of some activity, and he took apartments just opposite in the Chiaga, so that he could watch the mountain through a telescope.

He consulted the most experienced guide, named Salvatori, and after waiting for a fortnight was told that the time was ripe for an ascent. Wishing to see as much as he could, he decided to save himself as much physical exertion as possible, so used horses and mules where practicable, employing men to carry him in a chair 'up the steep slope of the cone of ashes'. In this way he saw much of the upper part in the afternoon and evening of one day, then slept for a few hours in a hut, reaching the summit before sunrise.

'It was still almost dark: we stood upon the irregular edge of a vast gulf spread out below at the depth of about 500 feet. The plain at the bottom would have been invisible but for an irregular network of bright red cracks spread over the whole of its surface. Now and then the silence was broken by a rush upwards of a flight of red-hot scoria from the diminutive crater within the larger one. These missiles, however, never extended themselves much beyond the small cavity from which they issued.'

Charles had noted large accumulations of congealed lava resembling huge steps, so decided to descend by this means. Salvatori, however, firmly declined to accompany him, so was left at the top with his colleagues, an excellent arrangement from Charles's point of view, because he could exercise discipline over the other guides and exert enough force, if it were necessary, to lift Charles and a young Cambridge friend bodily up by the ropes.

The descent then began, Charles encumbered by a heavy barometer strapped to his back, 'looking much like Cupid's quiver, though rather heavier'. In his pocket he had a box sextant, and in a basket two or three thermometers, a measuring tape, a flask of whiskey and a few biscuits.

Proceeding cautiously to the bottom of the 'steps', he then had to slide down a steep incline of fine sand, which was moving, so that he could not stand, the barometer being swept from his back. Soon, however, 'gravity had at last done its work and become powerless'. He dug himself out and found his barometer.

He was now, with his companion, on a burning plain, elliptical in shape, interspersed with intersecting ditches from which issued malodorous fumes. Assembling his few instruments, he proceeded to ascertain the depth of the crater from its upper edge, taking his base-line from his walking stick, which he fixed in a crack in the scoria. By the time he had finished the walking stick was in flames.

He then noted and registered the eruptions of the small embryo volcano at the further end of the plain. These occurred at comparatively regular intervals. Immediately following an eruption he rushed to an opening which gave him access to the subsidiary crater. A huge projecting rock, forty or fifty feet below, prevented him from seeing any possible lava lake. After further reconnoitring he chose his moment to scramble down the rock, and found that it had indeed hidden from view the liquid lava he so much wished to see.

After a minute or two he found the heat of the rock and the radiation from the lava intolerable, and was almost choked by the sulphurous fumes. Retreating a few feet, he was able to watch with slightly more ease, but was again defeated by the heat, the fumes and the scanty time between one eruption and another. Such was the effect of the heat on a pair of thick boots he was wearing that when he tried to take them off on returning to Naples they fell to pieces.

On ascending, his own and his companion's greatest need was for a draught of cold water, but none was available, so they half choked themselves with the biscuits, and then, on his young friend's crying out for a glass of whiskey, Charles suddenly remembered his flask, which contained half a pint of Irish whiskey. He handed it over. Whiskey was not one of his favourite drinks, but while on a recent visit to Ireland it had proved the only available substitute for brandy.

While at Naples he found yet another object of interest, the Temple of Serapis at Puzzuoli, which he considered 'the most remarkable building upon the face of the earth'. He concluded that it had been 'built at or above the level of the Mediterranean in order to profit by a hot spring which supplied its numerous baths'. He made a careful survey, showing that it had at one time subsided at least twenty-five feet below the sea and remained for some time at that level, then risen to its former level and again subsided. He later embodied his findings in a paper on the *Geological Theory of the Isothermal Surfaces of the Earth.*

Interested in everything though he was, some things were naturally of more interest to him than others, but the latter, he knew, would be of interest to experts, so he often purchased specimens for them. On visiting the caves of Adelsburg in Styria, he procured six of the *proteus anguineus*, 'a creature living only in the waters of dark caverns, which has eyes, but the eyelids cannot open'. These 'pets', as he called them, he conveyed in large bottles full of river-water, which he changed every night, the bottles, enclosed in leather bags, being secured to the barouche seat of his calash. In spite of these precautions, the first died at Vienna and the second at Prague. The last two survivors expired at Berlin, where he suspected Richard Wright of giving them water from a well instead of from a river. He preserved the corpses in spirits and sent them to various university collections at home and abroad.

In Berlin he renewed acquaintance with Baron Alexander von Humboldt, whom he had first met in Paris, and who was now organizing a congress of philosophers. The great naturalist's kindness made a deep impression on him, for he delegated two young men to act as cicerones, thus enabling Charles to see everything he wished with perfect ease.

Once, after breakfasting with him, Charles accompanied Humboldt into his study, where his papers, like Charles's own, 'were lying apparently in great disorder upon the tables'. From this conglomeration Humboldt extracted an envelope and gave it to Charles for his own use. It bore a list of all the savants then in Berlin and others who were expected, so that he could select those whom he most wished to meet.

Walking up and down Unter den Linden one day they discussed the foibles of some of their learned acquaintances, Humboldt making many amusing but good-natured remarks. Then, shaking Charles's hand, he said in English: 'My dear friend, I think it may be as well that we should not speak of each other until we meet again.' They parted for a few hours and met again—at a concert of Mendelssohn's.

10

The Iron Duke in Support

*

ON HIS return to England at the end of 1828 Charles Babbage went to live at 1 Dorset Street, Manchester Square, previously the residence of Dr. Wollaston. There he was to remain for the rest of his life, leaving his children with his mother at 5 Devonshire Street. It seems that without Georgiana he could not bear to return to his former home.

While on the Continent he had instructed his bankers to advance any monies up to £1,000 that might be required for the difference engine. He was also in constant correspondence with Joseph Clement, who transmitted drawings and enquiries to him from time to time, to all of which he at once replied.

Matters, however, had not been going smoothly.

An article had appeared in *The Record* under the heading 'Calculating Machinery'. In this the writer stated that a sum of money had been advanced from the national funds for the purpose of enabling Mr. Babbage to complete his invention and calling on him or his friends for an account of the disposal of the money advanced, the inference being that the undertaking had failed and that the inventor was deliberately concealing it from the public eye. John Herschel, who had been superintending the machine in his friend's absence, chose *The Times* for his reply, because of its 'wide circulation' and 'high respectability'.

He said that having been entrusted with the disbursement of the current expenses he was able to state from certain knowledge that the whole of the sum originally advanced by the Government had been properly expended in the execution of

Augusta Ada, Countess of Lovelace, aged about twenty. From a portrait by Margaret Carpenter, formerly at Ockham Park.

Reproduced by kind permission of the Ministry of Public Buildings and Works

Number of Operation	Nature of Operation	Variables acted upon	Variables receiving results	Indication of change in the value on any Variable	Statement of Results	Data				
						$^1V_1$ $\circ$ 0 0 1	$^1V_2$ $\circ$ 0 0 2	$^1V_3$ $\circ$ 0 0 4	$^0V_4$ $\circ$ 0 0 0	^0V $\circ$ 0 0 0
						1	2	n		
1	$\times$	$^1V_2 \times {}^1V_3$	$^1V_4, {}^1V_5, {}^1V_6$	$\left\{\begin{array}{l}^1V_2 = {}^1V_2 \\ ^1V_3 = {}^1V_3\end{array}\right\}$	$= 2n \ldots\ldots\ldots\ldots\ldots$	$\ldots$	2	n	$2n$	2
2	$-$	$^1V_4 - {}^1V_1$	$^2V_4 \ldots\ldots$	$\left\{\begin{array}{l}^1V_4 = {}^2V_4 \\ ^1V_1 = {}^1V_1\end{array}\right\}$	$= 2n-1 \ldots\ldots\ldots\ldots$	1	$\ldots$	$\ldots$	$2n-1$	
3	$+$	$^1V_5 + {}^1V_1$	$^2V_5 \ldots\ldots$	$\left\{\begin{array}{l}^1V_5 = {}^2V_5 \\ ^1V_1 = {}^1V_1\end{array}\right\}$	$= 2n+1 \ldots\ldots\ldots\ldots$	1	$\ldots$	$\ldots$	$\ldots$	$2n+$
4	$\div$	$^2V_5 \div {}^2V_4$	$^1V_{11} \ldots\ldots$	$\left\{\begin{array}{l}^2V_5 = {}^0V_5 \\ ^2V_4 = {}^0V_4\end{array}\right\}$	$= \dfrac{2n-1}{2n+1}$	$\ldots$	$\ldots$	$\ldots$	0	0
5	$\div$	$^1V_{11} \div {}^1V_2$	$^2V_{11} \ldots\ldots$	$\left\{\begin{array}{l}^1V_{11} = {}^2V_{11} \\ ^1V_2 = {}^1V_2\end{array}\right\}$	$= \dfrac{1}{2} \cdot \dfrac{2n-1}{2n+1} \ldots\ldots\ldots$	$\ldots$	2	$\ldots$		
6	$-$	$^0V_{13} - {}^2V_{11}$	$^1V_{13} \ldots\ldots$	$\left\{\begin{array}{l}^2V_{11} = {}^0V_{11} \\ ^0V_{13} = {}^1V_{13}\end{array}\right\}$	$= -\dfrac{1}{2} \cdot \dfrac{2n-1}{2n+1} = A_0$	$\ldots$	$\ldots$	$\ldots$		
7	$-$	$^1V_3 - {}^1V_1$	$^1V_{10} \ldots\ldots$	$\left\{\begin{array}{l}^1V_3 = {}^1V_3 \\ ^1V_1 = {}^1V_1\end{array}\right\}$	$= n-1(=3) \ldots\ldots\ldots$	1	$\ldots$	n	$\ldots$	
8	$+$	$^1V_2 + {}^0V_7$	$^1V_7 \ldots\ldots$	$\left\{\begin{array}{l}^1V_2 = {}^1V_2 \\ ^0V_7 = {}^1V_7\end{array}\right\}$	$= 2+0 = 2 \ldots\ldots\ldots$	$\ldots$	2	$\ldots$		
9	$\div$	$^1V_6 \div {}^1V_7$	$^3V_{11} \ldots\ldots$	$\left\{\begin{array}{l}^1V_6 = {}^1V_6 \\ ^0V_{11} = {}^3V_{11}\end{array}\right\}$	$= \dfrac{2n}{2} = A_1$	$\ldots$	$\ldots$	$\ldots$		
10	$\times$	$^1V_{21} \times {}^3V_{11}$	$^1V_{12} \ldots\ldots$	$\left\{\begin{array}{l}^1V_{21} = {}^1V_{21} \\ ^3V_{11} = {}^3V_{11}\end{array}\right\}$	$= B_1 \cdot \dfrac{2n}{2} = B_1 A_1$	$\ldots$	$\ldots$	$\ldots$		
11	$+$	$^1V_{12} + {}^1V_{13}$	$^2V_{13} \ldots\ldots$	$\left\{\begin{array}{l}^1V_{12} = {}^0V_{12} \\ ^1V_{13} = {}^2V_{13}\end{array}\right\}$	$= -\dfrac{1}{2} \cdot \dfrac{2n-1}{2n+1} + B_1 \cdot \dfrac{2n}{2}$	$\ldots$	$\ldots$	$\ldots$		
12	$-$	$^1V_{10} - {}^1V_1$	$^2V_{10} \ldots\ldots$	$\left\{\begin{array}{l}^1V_{10} = {}^2V_{10} \\ ^1V_1 = {}^1V_1\end{array}\right\}$	$= n-2(=2) \ldots\ldots\ldots$	1	$\ldots$	$\ldots$		
13	$-$	$^1V_6 - {}^1V_1$	$^2V_6 \ldots\ldots$	$\left\{\begin{array}{l}^1V_6 = {}^2V_6 \\ ^1V_1 = {}^1V_1\end{array}\right\}$	$= 2n-1 \ldots\ldots\ldots\ldots$	1	$\ldots$	$\ldots$		
14	$+$	$^1V_1 + {}^1V_7$	$^2V_7 \ldots\ldots$	$\left\{\begin{array}{l}^1V_1 = {}^1V_1 \\ ^1V_7 = {}^2V_7\end{array}\right\}$	$= 2+1 = 3 \ldots\ldots\ldots$	1	$\ldots$	$\ldots$		
15	$\div$	$^2V_6 \div {}^2V_7$	$^1V_8 \ldots\ldots$	$\left\{\begin{array}{l}^2V_6 = {}^2V_6 \\ ^2V_7 = {}^2V_7\end{array}\right\}$	$= \dfrac{2n-1}{3} \ldots\ldots\ldots$	$\ldots$	$\ldots$	$\ldots$		
16	$\times$	$^1V_8 \times {}^3V_{11}$	$^4V_{11} \ldots\ldots$	$\left\{\begin{array}{l}^1V_8 = {}^0V_8 \\ ^3V_{11} = {}^4V_{11}\end{array}\right\}$	$= \dfrac{2n}{2} \cdot \dfrac{2n-1}{3} \ldots\ldots\ldots$	$\ldots$	$\ldots$	$\ldots$		
17	$-$	$^2V_6 - {}^1V_1$	$^3V_6 \ldots\ldots$	$\left\{\begin{array}{l}^2V_6 = {}^3V_6 \\ ^1V_1 = {}^1V_1\end{array}\right\}$	$= 2n-2 \ldots\ldots\ldots\ldots$	1	$\ldots$	$\ldots$		
18	$+$	$^1V_1 + {}^2V_7$	$^3V_7 \ldots\ldots$	$\left\{\begin{array}{l}^2V_7 = {}^3V_7 \\ ^1V_1 = {}^1V_1\end{array}\right\}$	$= 3+1 = 4 \ldots\ldots\ldots$	1	$\ldots$	$\ldots$		
19	$+$	$^3V_6 \div {}^3V_7$	$^1V_9 \ldots\ldots$	$\left\{\begin{array}{l}^3V_6 = {}^3V_6 \\ ^3V_7 = {}^3V_7\end{array}\right\}$	$= \dfrac{2n-2}{4} \ldots\ldots\ldots$	$\ldots$	$\ldots$	$\ldots$		
20	$\times$	$^1V_9 \times {}^4V_{11}$	$^5V_{11} \ldots\ldots$	$\left\{\begin{array}{l}^1V_9 = {}^0V_9 \\ ^4V_{11} = {}^5V_{11}\end{array}\right\}$	$= \dfrac{2n}{2} \cdot \dfrac{2n-1}{3} \cdot \dfrac{2n-2}{4} = A_3 \ldots$	$\ldots$	$\ldots$	$\ldots$		
21	$\times$	$^1V_{22} \times {}^5V_{11}$	$^0V_{12} \ldots\ldots$	$\left\{\begin{array}{l}^1V_{22} = {}^1V_{22} \\ ^0V_{12} = {}^2V_{12}\end{array}\right\}$	$= B_3 \cdot \dfrac{2n}{2} \cdot \dfrac{2n-1}{3} \cdot \dfrac{2n-2}{3} = B_3 A_3$	$\ldots$	$\ldots$	$\ldots$		
22	$+$	$^2V_{12} + {}^2V_{13}$	$^3V_{13} \ldots\ldots$	$\left\{\begin{array}{l}^2V_{12} = {}^0V_{12} \\ ^2V_{13} = {}^3V_{13}\end{array}\right\}$	$= A_0 + B_1 A_1 + B_3 A_3 \ldots\ldots$	$\ldots$	$\ldots$	$\ldots$		
23	$-$	$^2V_{10} - {}^1V_1$	$^3V_{10} \ldots\ldots$	$\left\{\begin{array}{l}^2V_{10} = {}^3V_{10} \\ ^1V_1 = {}^1V_1\end{array}\right\}$	$= n-3(=1) \ldots\ldots\ldots\ldots$	1	$\ldots$	$\ldots$		
					Here follows a repetiti					
24	$+$	$^4V_{13} + {}^0V_{24}$	$^1V_{24} \ldots\ldots$	$\left\{\begin{array}{l}^4V_{13} = {}^0V_{13} \\ ^0V_{24} = {}^1V_{24}\end{array}\right\}$	$= B_7 \ldots\ldots\ldots\ldots\ldots\ldots$	$\ldots$	$\ldots$	$\ldots$	$\ldots$	
25	$+$	$^1V_1 + {}^1V_3$	$^1V_3 \ldots\ldots$	$\left\{\begin{array}{l}^1V_1 = {}^1V_1 \\ ^1V_3 = {}^1V_3 \\ ^5V_6 = {}^0V_6 \\ ^5V_7 = {}^0V_7\end{array}\right.$	$= n+1 = 4+1 = 5 \ldots\ldots$ by a Variable-card. by a Variable-card.	1	$\ldots$	$n+1$	$\ldots$	

Part of diagram of Bernouilli numbers by the Countess of Lovelace the machine. This sum, however, was inadequate, the deficit having been supplied from the inventor's private purse. To those who were conversant with mechanism and were aware of the multitude of tools to be invented and constructed before machinery of a type never before known could be built on a large scale and with perfect precision, this would not appear extraordinary; nor that an expenditure of time, talent and money, far beyond that originally envisaged, might be necessary.

The work continued to make steady progress, but such was the extent and variety of mechanical movements to be contrived and executed, and such the perfection of workmanship required to ensure success when put together, that a very long time must still elapse, and very heavy expenditure incurred, before the machine could be completed. But, Herschel added, no suspicion of failure had arisen. On the contrary, every mechanical difficulty had been overcome and nothing had occurred to raise any doubt about its ultimate success. He concluded that even if the fact of national assistance (though inadequate) justified enquiry fairness demanded that it should be made in a spirit totally opposite to that which apparently pervaded the article in *The Record*.

So far from these accusations, so forcibly rebutted by Herschel, being the truth, the experience of four years had convinced Charles that he had taken far too sanguine a view of the nature of his task, and that it was essential to ask the Government for a further grant of money. As a preliminary step, being at that time in Italy, he wrote to his brother-in-law, Mr. Wolryche Whitmore, requesting him to communicate with Lord Goderich, the former F. J. Robinson, and the two had an interview, at which again no minute seems to have been made by either party, but Mr. Wolryche Whitmore writing to Charles, then in Rome, informed him that the interview was unsatisfactory, adding that Lord Goderich did not like to admit that there was any understanding at the time the £1,500 was advanced, or that further advances would be made by the Government.

On his return Charles lost no time in seeing Lord Goderich, who at once, according to Buxton, 'most fairly admitted' that the understanding of what had taken place in 1823 was not very definite. Charles therefore approached the Duke of Wellington, now Prime Minister.

In the victor of Waterloo Charles found a sympathetic supporter and they remained firm friends for the rest of the Duke's life, the reason being undoubtedly that His Grace, unlike other members of the Establishment, was able to grasp the principles and capabilities of the machine. Years later, when he took the Countess of Wilton to see it, she asked Charles to explain his greatest difficulty in contriving it. Charles had never asked himself the question, but knew the nature of it well: it arose, he said, from the almost innumerable combinations among all the parts—'a number so vast, that no human mind could examine them all'. It occurred to him that a general commanding a vast army would be faced by a similar problem; and as he ceased talking to Lady Wilton this suspicion was confirmed. 'I know that difficulty well,' murmured the Duke.

With the Duke in mind, Charles was later to put these ideas in writing: the great commander must have studied and estimated the character of the enemy as well as that of his allies, he said, and scrutinized the secret motives actuating their respective governments; his knowledge of human nature must enable him to select the most capable and place them in the most advantageous positions; his knowledge of the means of contributing to the health and comfort of his troops must enable him to sustain their morale; in the field he must rapidly assess the force necessary to concentrate upon each of many points at any given time, and foresee the enemy's ability to do the same thing; he must then achieve the most difficult of mental tasks, that of classifying and grouping the innumerable combinations to which both sides might have recourse for attack or defence and, having done so, choose the most favourable; then, finding his plan ruined by some chance element, he must be able in the middle of the action to reorganize and carry out an entirely different plan. The genius that could meet and overcome such difficulties *must* be intellectual, said Charles, and would, under different circumstances, have been distinguished in many a different career.

In this way the ideas of many modern computer experts,

including the boffins playing their war games in the Pentagon, were anticipated well over a century ago by Charles Babbage and the Duke of Wellington.

His first contact with the Duke was in the early part of 1829, and Wellington referred the question of a further grant to the Royal Society, asking them to report on the present state of the machine and the possibility of completing it, this being accompanied by a statement from Charles to the effect that he had already spent about £6,000 on the machine.

The inevitable committee was appointed, this time including some professional engineers, and consisting of Mr. Davies Gilbert (President), Dr. Roget, Captain Sabine, John Herschel (chairman), Mr. Bailey, Mr. Brunel, Captain Kater, Mr. Donkin, Mr. Penn, Mr. Rennie, Mr. Barton and Mr. Warburton, Dr. Whewell being subsequently added. These gentlemen inspected the drawings, tools and the finished parts of the machine, and reported that they had no hesitation in saying that whatever the engine did it would do truly: in fact, so far from being surprised by the time it had taken to bring it to its present state, they felt more disposed to wonder how it had been possible to accomplish so much.

The drawings, some of them of the most elaborate description, formed a large and most essential part of the work; they were executed with extraordinary care and precision, and could be regarded as among the best that had ever been made, covering upwards of 400 square feet of surface. A period of three years was cautiously suggested as 'probably sufficient for its completion'. Of the adequacy of the machinery to work under all the friction and strain to which it could fairly be exposed the Committee had no doubt. And in commenting on the 'admirable workmanship' they remarked that anything inferior would have jeopardized the undertaking. It was very judicious of Mr. Babbage—though, of course, very expensive—'to admit of nothing but the very best and most finished work in every part: a contrary course would have been false economy and might have led to the loss of the whole capital expended upon it'.

Taking everything into consideration, it was suggested that perhaps three-fifths of the work was already accomplished, though this could not be said with any degree of certainty. As regards expense, a probable conjecture might be based on the same proportion, but again this should be received with very great latitude. But of the engine itself the Committee regarded it 'as likely to fulfil the expectations entertained of it by its inventor'. The report was signed by its chairman, John Herschel.

A second grant of £1,500 was thereupon made 'to enable him to complete the machine'. Unfortunately, like most grants, it was not enough. And in spite of his year on the Continent Charles was already beginning to feel the strain. Writing to a friend on 1st March 1829 he again spoke of ill health, saying that the medical men were urging him to lay aside his work and rest; he considered that he might live two years or conceivably twenty more, but he must cure the new complaint and finish the machine.

In consequence of this it was decided to call a meeting of some of his personal friends, and this took place on 12th May 1829. These were the Duke of Somerset, F.R.S., Lord Ashley, M.P., later the Earl of Shaftesbury, philanthropist, Sir John Franklin, discoverer of the North-West Passage, Mr. Wolryche Whitmore, M.P., Dr. Fitton, F.R.S., Mr. Francis Baily, F.R.S., and John Herschel, F.R.S.

Their object was to examine Charles's relation to the Government on the one hand and to the engineers and workmen employed by him on the other; and also to the general situation arising from the fatal misunderstanding at his original interview with the Chancellor in 1823. They decided that he embarked on the work because he believed that the Government wished him to do so and that by advancing £1,500 at the outset he imagined that further payments would be made from time to time, as the work required, and to secure him from personal loss. From the beginning he had worked assiduously and arduously on the undertaking, to the injury of his health and the neglect and refusal of other profitable occupations. So far as he could see, a further sum of at least £4,000 was still required before the machine could be completed; his private fortune, in his friends' opinion, was not sufficient to justify this sacrifice, taking into consideration not only his own interest but that of his family dependent on him. They concluded that a direct and personal application should be made to His Grace the Duke of Wellington, and that if this appeal proved unsatisfactory then they must regard Mr. Babbage as no longer called upon to continue with an undertaking which might be the ruin of his health and the impairment, if not the ruin, of his fortune.

In response to this the Duke, accompanied by Mr. Goulburn and Lord Ashley, inspected the engine, the drawings and other parts in progress. The Duke at once recommended a further grant of £3,000.

Charles Babbage was now satisfied that the Government had adopted his own view of what had happened in 1823, 'and', writes Buxton, 'it seems hardly possible to assign any other interpretation to what then took place'. Bitter experience, however, had made Charles more cautious, and in his anxiety to prevent the recurrence of any further misunderstanding he wrote to Goulburn towards the end of November 1829, proposing some ideas for expediting completion of the engine:

1. It should be considered the property of the Government.

2. Professional engineers should be appointed by the Government to examine the charges made for the work already executed, as well as for the future, and that such charges should be defrayed by the Government.

3. Under this arrangement he should continue to direct the construction of the engine. He added that he had been obliged to suspend the work for nearly nine months, and that such delay risked its final completion.

Mr. Goulburn's reply in December 1829 was very unsatisfactory. The Government, he said, could not, consistently with the principles on which he had been rendered assistance in the construction of the machine and without considerable inconvenience, adopt Mr. Babbage's proposals. The view of the Government was that aid had been given to assist an able and ingenious man of science, whose zeal had induced him to exceed the limits of prudence in the construction of a work which would, if successful, redound to his honour and be of great public advantage.

Lord Ashley, the bearer of these tidings, remarked: 'This is a wrong view of the position in which Mr. Babbage was placed after his conference with Lord Goderich, which must be explained to Mr. Goulburn.' Charles's reply was to refer to his own statement in his original letter to Sir Humphry Davy, 'whether I shall construct a large engine of this kind, and bring to perfection the others I have described, will in a great measure depend on the nature of the encouragement I may receive'.

This, however, was not a good argument. Having gone to the lengths he already had, the inference was that he *must* have received adequate encouragement. He also enquired of the Chancellor what, on receipt of the £3,000, were the claims which the Government would have on his engine or himself? Would he, Charles Babbage, owe the £6,000 or any part of that sum to the Government? Who owned the existing part of the machine—the Government or Charles Babbage? Did the Government expect him to continue to construct it at his own expense? Supposing he declined to continue, who owned the drawings and parts already made?

In January 1830 he wrote to Lord Goderich stating that Mr. Goulburn would probably apply to him about the interview in July 1823. The matter, he agreed, was left largely indefinite, and he (Charles Babbage) had never contended that any promise was made to him, but he always considered that whatever difficulties he might encounter it could never happen that he should ultimately suffer any pecuniary loss.

There was the usual delay and then on 24th February 1830 Lord Ashley told him what had been decided. Although the Government would not pledge themselves to *complete* the machine, they were willing to declare it their property. They were willing to advance £3,000 more than the sum (£6,000) already granted. When the machine was completed they would attend to any claim of Mr. Babbage to remuneration, either by bringing the matter before the Treasury or the House of Commons. Finally, professional engineers would be appointed to examine the bills. This seemed, even to Charles Babbage, a very fair arrangement and work was resumed on the machine.

In the same year he was sounded by Henry, Lord Brougham, then Lord Chancellor, about a knighthood. Having been summoned to Brougham's house, he found the carriage waiting at the door. They entered, and as they drove along Brougham observed that he had been asked to get several people connected with science knighted, and that it would be absurd unless persons like John Herschel and himself accepted. He therefore wished to know what Charles thought about it.

Charles replied with complete honesty but characteristic tactlessness that knighthood, which was bestowed on mayors of towns and upon all sorts of persons for all sorts of services, was by no means desirable as a reward for the highest science. He suggested that if anything of the kind were done it ought to be the institution of an order admitting those who, without any official position, uninfluenced by any duty, had at their own expense and by their own genius greatly extended the limits of human knowledge. Brougham agreed with the principle, but felt there would be considerable difficulty in carrying such a measure.

The Chancellor then asked him to mention the offer of knighthood to John Herschel, to which Charles replied that as Herschel's father had been knighted by George III he thought that his friend would find considerable difficulty in declining the honour. For himself, he added, he had 'no wish to join the circle of the B-Knighted'.

At a subsequent levee half a dozen knights were created, Charles's place being taken by Harris Nicolas, then secretary, and afterwards Chancellor, of the Order of the Ionian Islands, who told Charles that owing to his official position it was his duty to seek the otherwise 'very doubtful honour'.

Charles concluded his unfinished memorandum, dated 18th October 1865, by saying:

'The honourable distinctions of this country are curiously arranged. Their laws are made by officials and therefore for officials. It appears scarcely credible, yet it is literally true, that none but *mercenaries* can become members of the Order of the Bath. No merit however great can——'

Here, unfortunately, he broke off. Enough remains, however, to show what he really thought about knighthood and the Order of the Bath.

11

The Unhappy Art of Making Enemies

*

*D*URING the years in which he was working on the innumerable problems of the difference engine Charles
Babbage became involved in a number of scientific con-
troversies, and the fact that he was frequently in the right did
nothing to increase his popularity. If only for the sake of his own
career he would have done better to say nothing and refrain
from showing pique and resentment, as he unfortunately did
on some occasions.

In 1826, while his wife and father were still alive, he had
hoped to achieve three things: to win one of the first two
Royal Medals of the Royal Society with his paper on mechanical notation, which otherwise he would not have published
at that time; to become a secretary of the Royal Society; and
to be elected Lucasian Professor of Mathematics. He was
unsuccessful in all three, and took his defeat very badly.

The medals, founded by King William IV, were to be
awarded for 'the most important discoveries or series of investigations completed and made known to the Royal Society
in the year preceding the day of the award'. This resolution,
made on 26th January 1826, considerably reduced the number
of potential competitors, and Charles felt that he had an
excellent chance of winning. He carefully drew up his paper
On a Method of Expressing by Signs the Action of Machinery and
read it on 16th March 1826. He was 'simple enough', he
said, 'to expect that the Council of the Royal Society would
not venture upon a fraud on the very first occasion of exercising
the royal liberality', but on 16th November 1826 he was dis-

illusioned, the Council which had made the law violating it by awarding one of the two medals to Dalton, whose tabulation of the atomic weights of various elements had been made twenty years before, the other to James Ivory for his paper on refractions published three years earlier.

Worse was to happen. He had been promised the junior secretaryship of the Royal Society by Sir Humphry Davy, John Herschel being the senior secretary. The latter, in concert with Edward Ryan, who had married Georgiana's sister, were actively promoting his interests, but, in spite of Davy's promise, his fate was in the balance.

On 17th November Herschel wrote:

'Davy appears to have no intention to press the appointment of Children. He says himself that C's health is such that he does not imagine he could hold the office six months and has declared his intention to refer the appointment entirely to the Council, so that I count on your election as sure.' Herschel concluded with 'kind regards to Mrs. B.' [*sic*]

Three days later, however, Edward Ryan wrote to him, care of the Post Office, Birmingham—he seems to have been on a round of visits to the Isaacs at Boughton and the Wolryche Whitmores at Dudmaston—informing him that 'nothing had been done by your friends, and I think your chance not good, but do not act on these few hasty lines in any way. . . . No election will take place at the Royal until the 30th, and Colby thinks that your attendance before is not necessary.'

This letter from Ryan was followed by another, dated 24th November, breaking the bad news:

'It is decided that you are *not* to be the secretary as Mr. Children is. Herschel at my request gives you a detail of the proceedings. . . . I have been delighted with Herschel's conduct, he has been a most zealous and active friend throughout. Next I should tell you that you have in no way whatever been compromised. You might have been Secretary had your friends chosen to have jobbed at all, but they decided that you should only come in on the highest ground and that the President should feel the weight of the opinion of the Society and *name* you himself, or that you should not be put in nomination.'

He then spoke in uncomplimentary terms of Davy's character. The inventor of the safety lamp, who was of humble origin and had married a wealthy widow in 1812, was noted for his deference to rank and title; worse still, he was not very scrupulous in monetary matters.

Ryan continued:

'The President has behaved infamously, full of his tricks and knavery of every description and treating Herschel with great indignity. The Society, every member almost, as Colby and Herschel inform me, are in the greatest rage at the President's proceedings and nothing now is talked of but removing him.'

Ryan was also very much annoyed that Charles had lost so much money for the present.

John Herschel, on 25th November, said that Children's name was the only one on the house list 'when the matter was irregularly brought by the President before a meeting of eight or nine persons whom he chose to call a Council, appointed to meet "for a few minutes" before the usual hour of the Society's meetings "to transact some business connected with the Treasurer's Accounts" '. Herschel was anxious at present not to think of the past with annoyance but to the future with hope, a feeling which though at present rather sombre was rapidly changing into a resolve to place the future conduct of the society on a higher and better footing. This feeling was generated among all the scientific members and would have its full effect. 'Some good is developed even by the worst things that happen. You make that sometimes an argument for pushing them to the worst. I do not admit its force', said Herschel, adding: 'One good in these things is the display of character they produce.'

Charles recalled this episode in his autobiography nearly forty years later, saying that when Sir Humphry Davy announced that he proposed to fill the vacancy Dr. Wollaston asked him whether he claimed the nomination as a right of the President, to which Davy replied that he did and nominated Mr. Children.

'The President, as President', said Charles, 'has no such

right; and even if he had possessed it, he had promised Mr. Herschel that I should be his colleague. There were upright and eminent men on that Council; yet no one of them had the moral courage to oppose the President's dictation.'

In his letter of 25th November Herschel alluded to the third of Charles's aspirations at this time: 'Meanwhile, I hope you will get the Lucasian Professorship of which indeed there does now seem to be a fair prospect. By the bye, Young told Kater he was anxious you should, as you ought, to be Member of the Board of Longitude.'

There were three candidates for the Chair of Newton at this time: Charles Babbage, Dr. French, Master of Jesus College, Cambridge, and George Biddell Airy. According to Airy, Dr. French withdrew on Charles's threatening legal proceedings, thus leaving the field clear for the other two. 'At length, on 7th December 1826, the election . . . took place. I was elected (I think unanimously) and admitted', said Airy. Writing nearly thirty years later, Charles Babbage's other *bête noire*, Richard Sheepshanks, said he suspected Charles Babbage of never forgiving Airy 'for being preferred as Lucasian Professor and whose discharge of that office formed such a contrast to his own'. It would probably have been more correct to say that Babbage never forgave Airy for disparaging the difference engine.

Be this as it may, it is certain that these disappointments and his reaction to them gave him a reputation for disingenuousness, obstinacy and intransigence. And from this time onwards he determined to revenge himself on the Royal Society. Instead of acting on his own advice to Herschel in 1821 in a dispute between Sir James South and Dollond the instrument-maker, and desisting from 'pursuing a course calculated to obscure a splendid reputation', he deliberately prepared an attack on the man and the institution to whom he owed Government support for the difference engine. It is true that, apart from Davy's cheating him out of the secretary-ship, the Royal Society was in need of reform and that jobbery was rampant, but in the circumstances it was a question of taste, and Charles, unfortunately, when he felt that he had been

wronged was never a man to be deterred by any such consideration as this.

About the middle of 1830, by which time he had succeeded
Airy as Lucasian Professor, he published his *Reflections on the
Decline of Science in England and on Some of its Causes*. Although
he remarked that he was not hostile to the Royal Society, only
to the party which governed it, this did nothing to mitigate
what in the eyes of many people was an offence. The Council,
however, took no public notice of it, and politely thanked him
for sending a copy.

The book, like so much of Charles Babbage's writings,
contained some brilliant ideas, far ahead of their time, but
these were spoilt by being twisted to form a piece of special
pleading. In spite of England's eminence in mechanical and
manufacturing ingenuity, he said, she was much below other
nations in the more difficult and abstract sciences. This was
due partly to the system of education, and he suggested revised
methods at the University. Scientific knowledge scarcely
existed among the upper classes. The discussions in both
Houses of Parliament which arose on the occurrence of any
subject connected with science sufficiently proved this fact.

Up to this point few people could, in justice, have quarrelled
with him. But then he turned it into a recital of his own
grievances, comparing England with France under Napoleon,
to the glory of the latter, and mentioning other countries
where 'a knowledge of science is a recommendation to public
appointments and . . . a man does not make a worse ambassador because he has directed an observatory', whereas in
England political power was almost the only recommendation.
He analysed the numbers and positions of a number of savants,
their titles, decorations and marks of royal favour, among
them the Marquis Laplace, Carnot and the two Barons von
Humboldt.

He then made a direct attack on the Royal Society. The
greater a man's scientific achievements, he said, the better
his chance of being blackballed. He criticized an 'unexplained
job' of Sir Humphry Davy's, accusing him of lining his own
pocket at the Society's expense. (Davy had died in 1827, and

was therefore unable to defend himself.) He queried the election of Davy's successor, Davies Gilbert, 'a most amiable and kind hearted man', but not qualified for the Presidential chair. He damned the two secretaries, Dr. P. M. Roget and Captain E. Sabine, with faint praise, criticized the written minutes and the union of several offices in one person, the method of bestowing the Royal and Copley Medals, and attributing the Society's decline to its mismanagement by a party or coterie whose one object was to maintain itself in power.

Among his plans for reform was the limitation of the Society to a fair representation of the talent of the country, so that every vacancy would become an object of competition among persons of acknowledged merit. He also proposed the foundation of an Order of Merit, an idea of his, like many others, which has since been adopted.

The book naturally evoked much criticism and resentment. *The Times* of 8th July 1830 published a letter from Captain Kater saying that at a meeting of the Council of the Royal Society on 10th June he had asked what steps were to be taken respecting the book. To this the President replied that deeply as he regretted its 'injurious tendency' and disapproved of its 'uncandid spirit', and notwithstanding the violation of the statutes, which rendered the author liable to expulsion from the Society, he was unwilling, considering Mr. Babbage's past services to science, to proceed to this extremity, but thought it more consistent with the dignity of the Society to take no further notice of the matter. Like the Grand Duke of Tuscany, Davies Gilbert no doubt deeply sympathized with him over his terrible bereavement, and made allowances on this account.

His magnanimous decision was accepted by Captain Kater, who replied that no one could have a higher respect for Mr. Babbage's scientific attainments than he had, and that he had been in the habit of the most friendly intercourse with him for many years; he nevertheless wished to mention the names of the present members of the Council and to pray for their re-election in the following November. (Some of them—Sir John

Franklin, Dr. Pond, George Rennie, Dr. Roget, Henry Warburton and Kater himself—had served on one or other of the
committees which had recommended the difference engine
for Government grants.)

In the following year an ably written pamphlet appeared
anonymously. The author was Professor G. Moll of Utrecht,
who gently chided Charles for criticizing his fellow countrymen, saying that a very different opinion of them was held
abroad, and he specifically cited Sir Humphry Davy and John
Herschel.

He then corrected some of Charles's more naive errors.
The nobility of no country was much interested in science, he
remarked. It had been the almost invariable custom in every
country that people holding high office were taken from a
certain rank in society. Whenever another principle was
adopted it was in times of revolution, or in very extraordinary
cases. 'It is the count, the marquis, the baron, the minister,
who is a philosopher,' said Moll, 'but it is not the philosopher
who, on account of his philosophy, is raised to the rank of an
ambassador, or a count, or a baron or a minister.'

Alexander von Humboldt, Chancellor to the King of
Prussia, was a baron by birth, he explained. As for the
Frenchmen, Laplace, Carnot, Chaptal and Cuvier, the case
was very different. All their great scientific achievements
preceded the rise of Napoleon. The latter, after abolishing the
Republic, tried to win over all men of talent, and Laplace, for
example, was made Minister of the Interior, but proved so
inefficient that he had to be removed. It was profitable for
these men, yes; honourable, no.

As for an Order of Merit, did Mr. Babbage really imagine
that Dr. Wollaston or Dr. Maskelyne would have been more
respected either at home or abroad if, like the Russians, he
had half a dozen different-coloured ribbons pending on his
breast? enquired Dr. Moll. In almost every country where
such distinctions existed half the ribbons were given for jobbing
and patronage. Fools, he said, were very eager to have them,
but really meritorious men did not attach the slightest value
to them.

The King of England, if he were inclined to science, and wished to treat its professors with distinction, might confer upon them the honour of knighthood or of the baronetcy, and, added Dr. Moll: 'There can be little doubt, if once the calculating machine can be brought to perfection, but that we are going to have a Sir Charles Babbage.'

The only effect of these strictures was to strengthen Charles's curious obsession; nothing, it seems, less than a peerage and the Garter would have satisfied him. Yet twenty years later he said with perfect truth: 'Of all steps in the social scale, that which first elevates a man into the class of gentleman is by far the greatest . . . even the peerage to a private gentleman is not so great an advance.'

Why, then, one is tempted to ask, did he, a man of supreme genius, care so much about a peerage? There is no answer. It is just one of those enigmas which nature throws up from time to time to puzzle less gifted mortals.

Others were not to show him the magnanimity of Davies Gilbert and the Royal Society. About this time, according to Professor De Morgan, he accused some members of the Royal Astronomical Society of being in a conspiracy against him. These were Professor Airy and the Rev. Richard Sheepshanks, Fellow of Trinity College, Cambridge.

In 1829 Sir James South, owner of the Campden Hill Observatory, was elected President of the Society, but a clique, hostile to him and in an attempt to thwart him, made Sheepshanks secretary. Sir James, whose behaviour bordered at times on the mentally deranged, was a crony of Charles's, and the latter supported him, thereby, to quote his own words, becoming involved in 'a quarrel in which I had no part'. Confronting Charles one day in March 1831, Sheepshanks told him: 'I am determined to put down Sir James South, and if you and other respectable men will give him your support I will put you down.'

During 1832 a large equatorial mounting was constructed by Troughton & Simms for South's twelve-inch object glass. South complained that it was not satisfactory, but (according to Charles) all might have remained good friends had it not been for Sheepshanks, who, having a personal quarrel with South, forced himself on to Troughton & Simms as their adviser and with his friend Professor Airy constantly obtruded themselves at Campden Hill to examine the instrument. This prevented all hope of reconciliation, and the parties had recourse to the King's Bench, Troughton & Simms bringing an action to recover payment. Sheepshanks, having studied law, acted as adviser. The court recommended arbitration, and this dragged on from 1833 to 1838, Troughton dying in the meantime, and South finally having to pay the bill. Various senior wranglers took part as counsel, the arbitrator, Frederick Maule, being 'crack senior wrangler of his time', *vide* Sheepshanks, 'the Laplace of England'.

Charles, after first refusing to become a witness for South, was finally persuaded to do so, and was, he said, like other witnesses for the defence, intimidated by Sheepshanks. On the seventeenth day of the arbitration Sheepshanks told him that it was necessary to discredit him because he had supported Sir James South, adding that he would at a future time attack him publicly on another subject on account of the part he had taken in this matter.

Again, according to Charles, whose persecution complex was not wholly due to imaginary causes, as will be seen later on, a system of disparagement was maintained against all who supported Sir James. 'One man was alarmed by the fear that some inaccuracies in his astronomical publications should be criticized. Of another it was hinted that his mathematics were all wrong.'

That Charles Babbage had a paranoic tendency there can be no doubt. But there is also no doubt that Sheepshanks and Airy remained his enemies for life, and that Airy, who was frequently consulted on scientific matters by the Government, was by far the more dangerous of the two.

12

Clement Downs Tools

*

MEANWHILE, if Charles Babbage was satisfied with the new arrangements for the machine, Joseph Clement was not. The engineer had been delivering his accounts in such a state of confusion that it was found impossible to judge the accuracy of his charges.

Clement had invented tools for making parts of the difference engine. He had also trained a set of workmen in their use. He had received from Charles Babbage for several years £30 a month, and was therefore his employee. Since everything was precision-built, it was costly and slow, and Charles, smarting under charges amounting to fraud and dishonesty, attributed the slow progress and misfortunes of the machine to what he considered the exorbitant charges of Clement. The latter, on the other hand, asserted that he had never been so badly paid in his life. Others, however, had questioned his charges, not always with success, for he was a first-rate craftsman who believed that the labourer was worthy of his hire.

He once received an order from an American to construct a large screw in the best possible manner, and carried this out so literally and with such mathematical accuracy that the bill amounted to some hundreds of pounds. The American, who had never contemplated paying more than £20, objected, so the matter was referred to arbitrators, who decided in favour of Clement.

Writing on 9th November 1869 Charles said:

'Since the year 1816 I have never been without a drawing office and workshop attached to my dwelling house, in which

I have constantly worked myself and have also employed highly skilled workmen to assist me. In these shops the contrivance of new and more effective tools has thus been unremittingly followed out.

'I have heard at different times from men I had employed in former years that amongst their own class it was frequently said that "Mr. Babbage made Clement; Clement made Whitworth; Whitworth made the tools".

'When I first employed Clement he possessed one lathe (a very good one) and his workshop was in a small front kitchen. When I ceased to employ him, he valued his tools at several thousand pounds, and he had converted a large chapel into a workshop. Whitworth has made a fortune of which he spends with great liberality.'

A statement of Clement's accounts to December 1830, sent by Charles to the Chancellor of the Exchequer, shows how much of the expense of the machine was attributable, then as now, to labour costs.

				£	s.	d.
Expense to the end of 1824	..	..	..	£ 600	0	0
Expense to the end of 1827	..	..	..	521	16	9
Mr. Clement's bills to June 1827	..	..	..	4775	13	3
Mr. Clement's bills to 9th May 1829	..	..	730	12	2
				6628	2	2
Deduct old tools sold	..			36	4	0
				6591	18	2
Mr. Clement's bill to December 1830 about	..		600	0	0
				£7191	18	2

One of the engineers, Mr. Maudsley, appointed to examine the bills, fell ill and the report was delayed, whereupon Clement informed Charles that should the money remain unpaid much longer he would be obliged from want of funds to discharge some of the workmen. In conveying this news to the Treasury

Charles took the opportunity of suggesting that since it was now absolutely necessary to find additional room for the erection of the machine, it might be better to remove the works to the neighbourhood of his own residence. There was also another reason why this should be done; namely, the safety of the machine and drawings, now that they were Government property. No precautions had so far been taken to ensure their safety from fire or other damage while in Clement's custody, whose workshop was a considerable distance from Dorset Street.

Their Lordships' reply was sent to the Royal Society, confirming that the machine was the property of the Government, who proposed to defray the further expense necessary to its completion; that the machine was to be inspected and its progress noted, together with the extent of any further sum that might be necessary for its completion. The letter was referred to the previous committee appointed to inspect the machine, with the addition of Sir John Lubbock and Mr. Troughton. They met Charles at Clement's workshop in Prospect Place, Lambeth, and agreed with all his proposals.

Some land adjoining the garden at Dorset Street in East Street, Manchester Square, being pronounced suitable by an experienced surveyor, a lease of it was subsequently granted by Charles to the Government. Work began on the construction of a fireproof building, capable of containing the engine and its drawings, with the necessary workshops and offices.

For a time work continued harmoniously on the engine, the greater part of it being executed by Joseph Clement under Charles Babbage's immediate direction. On Clement's bills being received they were forwarded to two notable engineers, Messrs. Donkin and Field, who had been appointed by the Government to check them and report on their accuracy. When they were approved and certified Charles transmitted them to the Treasury, and warrants, made out to him, were thereupon issued.

The system was so slow and cumbersome that it soon proved an embarrassment to the smooth working of the undertaking. Charles was perpetually badgered for advances by

Clement, whose accounts were allowed to stand over. As Clement's interest lessened, Charles's anxiety grew, especially when it transpired that the engineer was unable or unwilling to pay his workmen without prompt payment of his own demands. In order to prevent delay Charles advanced money from time to time out of his own pocket so that the Government was constantly indebted to him. These sums were eventually repaid but the irregularity in meeting Clement's demands was a constant source of annoyance and tended to distract Charles's attention from his own work.

The fireproof buildings and workshops having in the meantime been erected, he now proposed to remove the engine, so far as it was completed, and at the same time told Clement that in future he must rely solely upon the payments to be made by the Treasury.

Clement thereupon made the most extravagant demands for compensation for having to carry on the work at East Street. These were so exorbitant as to be ridiculous and they could not be met. His immediate reaction was to cease work on the machine and dismiss the workmen. In a letter which he wrote to Charles his tone was insolent and offensive.

31 St. George's Road,
Southwark.
26th March 1833

Sir,

After what passed between you and I on Wednesday last respecting settling my account you then stated that you could not pay me as you had not received the money from Government. I said that I had nothing to do with Government respecting the calculating machine, that you were the only person that had given me any orders respecting the calculating machine, that you were the only person I had made my accounts out to and the only person who had paid my accounts, that you were responsible to me for all expense incurred on the machine up to the present time, and that it would be impossible for me to proceed much further without money.

Your answer was that for the future you would never advance or pay me a single shilling on your own account respecting the machine.

Now after that declaration I do not think that I should be justified in proceeding any further with the calculating machine until someone is made responsible to me for the work that may be done hereafter. I therefore gave notice the following morning to all the men employed on the calculating machine that I should not be able to employ them after this week as there was a misunderstanding between you and me. Now if it be a misunderstanding, I hope for the sake of my men and the machine that you will be pleased to take the earliest opportunity of arranging things in a more satisfactory manner.

> I remain,
> Dear Sir,
> Your obedient servant
> (signed) Joseph Clement

P.S. I should have written to you sooner had my health permitted.

To C. Babbage Esq.

This was a most serious blow and Charles had no course but to take up the matter with the Treasury, who agreed that the best thing to do was to remove the drawings and all parts of the engine to East Street, and then to arrange a plan of payment of Clement's current demands in such a manner as to prevent the serious inconvenience which had hitherto attended their own tardy system.

Clement, however, thought otherwise. Although for years he had been an employee, he withdrew from the undertaking altogether, refusing to surrender the valuable tools used in the work, many of which had been invented by Charles to meet the novel forms and combinations associated with the difference engine. This, extraordinary and unjust though it may appear to be, Clement had a legal right to do. Even when the cost of construction had been defrayed by their employers, engineers and mechanics had the right of property to all the tools constructed by themselves.

An offer was made to surrender the tools for a given sum, but this Clement also refused. Moreover, Charles was deprived not only of his tools but also of his drawings. From 1834 onwards all work on the machine was suspended.

13

Bottom of the Poll

*

WHILE he was having these differences with Joseph Clement, Charles, with characteristic and inexhaustible energy, became involved in politics.

After the passing of the Reform Bill in May 1832 there was a dissolution of Parliament, and at the ensuing election he became, for the second time, chairman of the London Committee for Henry Cavendish, second wrangler and senior Smith's prizeman, candidate for the University of Cambridge.

These experiences, together with those at Bridgnorth on behalf of his brother-in-law Mr. Wolryche Whitmore, gave him a wide and cynical knowledge of the constitution and behaviour of committees, the gist being that only a few men did the difficult and real work; but occasionally a few honest men were found, who were useful as adjuncts to give a kind of high moral tone to the cause, though they were usually considered bores and crotchety fellows by the more worldly members.

Considering these views of his it is all the more curious that he consented to become a candidate himself; and was, indeed, optimistic about his chances. Writing to a friend at Kingston, Jamaica, on 7th July 1832, he said it was not impossible that he might have a seat in the next Parliament and would like to know what measures would be most conducive to the speedy abolition of slavery, having regard to the personal security of both the white and black population.

During the discussions on Parliamentary reform he had become, from honest conviction, a reformer himself, and the explanation of his action must be that he was naive enough to think that in a *reformed* Parliament human nature would suddenly undergo a change for the better; yet, although a Liberal, his views were far from extreme, according to Buxton. He had no prophetic visions of political perfectability and indulged in no extravagant expectations of any miraculous amelioration of the condition of mankind through the means of party strife or violent dislocation of political machinery. He knew that Parliamentary duties would encroach on his scanty leisure and involve him in engagements incompatible with his scientific studies. He knew that if elected he must either neglect the difference engine or relinquish, at least for a time, all work upon it. Knowing all this, he yet allowed himself to be nominated for the borough of Finsbury.

Parliament was prorogued by commission on 16th October 1832 and dissolved on 3rd December, the candidates for the new Parliament being returnable on 29th January 1833. There were four for Finsbury: Charles Babbage, Mr. Thomas Duncombe, Mr. Wakly, editor of *The Lancet*, a Radical Reformer, and Mr. Pownall, a magistrate.

According to Charles Babbage himself, 'few incidents worth note occurred'. The only one that he bothered to record tells how, on returning one day in an omnibus from the City to his committee room on Holborn Hill, he was able to acquire a few votes. The situation was a familiar one today. A man had nothing less than a sovereign and asked the conductor for change. There was the usual difficulty and finally Charles offered the loan of a sixpence, together with a copy of one of his election addresses. Both were accepted with alacrity and demands were made by other passengers for copies of the address. Votes were promised and, in fact, he believed that he had carried the whole of his fellow passengers with him, for he left the omnibus to the accompaniment of hearty cheers.

A year or so later the man to whom he had lent the sixpence wrote to say that he had watched the Finsbury election with interest and suggested that Charles Babbage would be favourably received in the borough of Stroud, where there was an approaching vacancy, and where the writer would give his fullest support. Charles, having by this time had his fill of politics, declined the kind offer with thanks.

In fact, much more happened than Charles Babbage led his readers to suppose. It was rumoured, for example, that John Cam Hobhouse, friend of Lord Byron, had declined the poll in favour of Charles Babbage. This was finally scotched only when Hobhouse wrote on 26th June 1833 categorically denying any such thing: 'Not so. I never could decline what I never contemplated.' Some Finsbury gentlemen had asked him to be put in nomination for that borough, Hobhouse explained, but on coming to London he found Mr. Babbage and Mr. Duncombe in the field, and wrote to both, begging that no steps would be taken to bring him forward. Both candidates were his friends, and he would not oppose *either* of them. Mr. Duncombe had behaved in a very friendly fashion towards him at Westminster and to Mr. Babbage he was under personal obligations.

Another rumour was unfortunately never killed. Charles Babbage was constantly accused on the hustings of misappropriating public funds granted for the difference engine. This caused him more pain and distress than anything else.

But even the first canvass satisfied him that he had embarked on a sea of trouble. He was asked to give so many inconsistent pledges that in order to carry them out he would have had to sacrifice all pretensions to popularity or else make utterly worthless promises. The mere word 'reform' had roused the wildest dreams among all classes, and extravagant expectations had been created: while violent passions engendered by party conflict were at their height. To surrender on any one point would have meant sacrificing his independence. This, in his disillusionment, he saw and was not prepared to do. Inevitably he came bottom of the poll.

Duncombe	..	2,514
Pownall	..	1,915
Wakly	..	695
Babbage	..	379

The first two were returned.

The best thing to come out of it all was the electioneering squib or, as he described it, *jeu d'esprit*, entitled 'Politics and Poetry, or the Decline of Science'. The only disappointing thing about it is that he never introduces the philosophers. It shows, nevertheless, that whatever sort of novelist he might have made, the stage lost a dramatist of some wit and talent; and nothing, not even his autobiography, reveals more of the author's character and versatility. Whereas the names of his *characters* were worthy of his hated enemy, Disraeli.

DRAMATIS PERSONAE

People of Fashion
  Turnstile, a retired Philosopher, M.P. for Shoreditch
  Lord Flumm, a Tory nobleman of ancient family
  Countess of Flumm, his wife
  Lady Selena, their daughter
  Hon. Mrs. Fubsey, sister of the Countess

Whigs
  Lord A., Prime Minister
  Closewind, First Lord of the Admiralty
  Shift, Secretary at War
  Smooth, Secretary for the Colonies, also M.P. for Shoreditch

Tories
  Lord George
  Lord Charles   } Members of the
  Marquis of Flamborough   } Conservative Club
  Dick Trim, a former Whipper-in

Shoreditch electors
  Highway, a Radical
  Griskin, Colonel of the Lumber Troop
  Tripes, his lieutenant

Philosophers

Sir Orlando Windfall, Knt.R.Han.Guelph Order. An astronomical observer

Sir Simon Smugg, Knt.R.Han.Guelph Order, Professor of Botanism Atall, an Episcopizing Mathematician, Dean of Canterbury Byeways, a Calculating Officer

Other Lords—Conservative and Whig

The scene is laid in the West End of London near the end of May 1835, and the piece opens in the committee room of the Conservatives. 'Does anybody know Turnstile?' Trim enquires. 'The Reform Member for Puddledock, isn't he?' mumbles Lord George, 'the author of a book on pin-making and things of that kind. An ironmonger in Newgate Street.' Trim corrects him. 'No, no. Member for Shoreditch, with Smooth, the Colonial Secretary.' Lord Charles, taking his cigar from his mouth, thinks he has heard something of him at Cambridge—Newtonian Professor of Chemistry when he was there. Couldn't he be talked over? Trim wonders. 'No, no, he is too sharp for that,' replies Lord Charles. 'Perhaps a hint of an appointment . . .' murmurs Flamborough. 'Nor that either,' retorts Lord Charles, 'he is a fellow of some spirit and devilish proud.' Trim considers him a sort of a philosopher that wants to be a man of the world.

Scene IV opens in Grosvenor Square. Turnstile enters, musing. 'This will never do. They make use of me and laugh at me in their sleeves; push me round and go by. . . . And where is this to end? What shall I have to show for it? Confounded loss of time; to hear those fellows prosing, instead of seeing the occultation last night. And that book of L's; so much that *I* had begun upon, and might have finished! It never will do! [Rousing himself after a pause.] But knowledge, after all, *is* power. That at least is certain—power—to do what? to refuse Lord Doodle's invitation; and to ask Lord Humbug for a favour, which it is ten to one he will refuse. But the Royal Society is defunct! That I have accomplished. Gilbert, and the Duke, and the Secretaries! I have driven them all before me!—and now, though *I* must not be a knight of the Guelphic Order (yet a riband is a pretty-looking thing and a star too!)—I will show that I can teach *them* how to make knights; and describe the decorations that other men are to wear.'

In order to get this very Independent Member to support them the Tories suddenly make much of Turnstile, and there is an amusing scene in Lady Flumm's drawing-room when Lady Selena expresses the hope, indeed, she feels sure, that he loves music, to which he replies: 'Not *very* particularly. I must acknowledge a barrel organ is an instrument most in my way.' He is won over, however, and promises to attend Lady Flumm's next party. Once outside the house, his conscience pricks. 'This is all very delightful; but what will they say at Shoreditch?— twice in one week absent from the House, and at two Tory parties.'

Griskin then appears, and hints that Turnstile might help him in a little job, to which the philosopher replies shortly: 'I am not acquainted with the Commander-in-Chief,' reflecting cynically: 'And this is your "reformed" Parliament.'

Act II, Scene I, is set in Downing Street, after a Cabinet meeting. Lord A., Closewind, Shift, Smooth and other Whigs are wondering how they can make use of this very Independent Member Turnstile, and discussing his possible appointment as President of the Board of Manufactures. Lord A. has been told that his claims are strong—long devotion to science, great expenditure and loss of time for public objects—high reputation, and weight of opinion—as a man of science. Smooth thinks that perhaps a *practical* man . . . 'And that,' says Shift, 'poor Turnstile is not. He must always have a *reason.*' Smooth presses the claims of MacLeech—seems to him to be the very man for the manufactures—a practical, persevering man of business.

Thus Turnstile is let down by everyone. In despair he asks Byeways' assistance, saying: 'Deserted by those shabby dogs the Radicals, and tricked, I fear, by the Whigs, I find I have no chance of a decent show of numbers at the next election if my scientific friends do not support me with spirit.' But Byeways, the Calculating Officer, fails him, too. And Lady Flumm tells the footman to put a note in the visiting book, saying: 'We are out of town,' whenever Mr. Turnstile calls.

A sadder and wiser Turnstile soliloquizes in his parlour: 'Then all is up. What a fool have I been to embark upon this sea of trouble! Two years of trifling and lost time; while others have been making discoveries and adding to their reputation. Those *rascal* Whigs, my blood boils to think of them. I can forgive the Shoreditch people—the greasy, vulgar, money-getting beasts; but my *friends*, the men of principle—[getting up and walking about]—Is it still too late to return? [Looking round upon his books and instruments.] There you are, my old friends, whom I *have* treated rather ungratefully. What a scene at that cursed meeting! Highway's bullying, and the baseness of Smooth; the sleek, sly steering of that knave MacLeech; and yet they *must* succeed. There's no help for it. I *am* fairly beaten —thrown overboard, with not a leg to stand upon; and all I have to do is to go to bed now, to sleep off this fever; and to-morrow, take leave of politics, and try to be myself once more.'

14

'To Be Myself Once More'

*

HE HAD, of course, to some extent always been himself, and his activities in the 1830s reveal the extraordinary range and versatility of his intellectual power. Nothing more was ever done to the difference engine, and although he turned his attention to other pursuits, none seems to have inspired any greater interest in his children. He seems to have been interested in them only when they were old enough to take an intelligent interest in his own activities.

In the summer of 1831 the sixteen-year-old Herschel was deputed to fetch his two small brothers, Dugald and Henry, now aged seven, from Worcestershire. The parting from Mrs. Powell at the lodge must have been very sad, though Henry did not mention it. The journey by coach was long and tedious, and Henry slept for most of the time, except when an old gentleman tickled him with a straw. When they reached London it was dark and the gas lamps were alight. Their father met them and took them, as far as Henry could recollect, to 5 Devonshire Street.

The following morning they were sent to Bruce Castle School at Tottenham, which was run by the brothers of Rowland Hill. There the two little boys remained for three or four years, spending their holidays at 5 Devonshire Street with their grandmother and sister. Henry feared his grandmother but loved Georgiana. Mrs. Babbage was usually up before the boys and called them every morning. They slept in separate beds in the same room and in winter the water in their jugs was often frozen over, a good excuse for less washing than usual. 'I suppose that we must occasionally have seen our father during the holidays', said Henry, thoughtfully, 'but I have no recollection of it.'

Then in the autumn of 1834 Georgiana died, her father's 'little Georgiana', his only daughter, whom he was going to find it difficult not to spoil; Georgiana, with her mother's name, who promised to have her mother's excellence, his only daughter. She was in her late teens and her death must have been a grievous blow to Charles. Only three of his seven sons now remained.

In January 1835 the two younger boys left Bruce Castle School and went to University College School. From there they were taken away for the summer holidays by their grandmother. Once they lodged in a cottage close to the beach at Hastings, the landlady's husband being in gaol for smuggling 'a little French glass'. In 1836 they were at Clifton, Bristol, during the British Association meeting, but did not see much of their father. Their aunt, Mrs. Hollier, came over from Wales, bringing her eldest daughter Henrietta. 'One day we were playing together on the terrace outside the house when my father came', said Henry. 'I do not remember what he said to us, but he put his hand on the head of Henrietta and said: "Well, my little one." She said: "He does not like us." Dugald and I made some sort of explanation, but Henrietta remained dissatisfied with him.' Charles's mind, no doubt, was on weightier matters.

In 1837 their grandmother took the two boys to Southsea, Portsmouth and Cowes and they had to transfer from the coach to the railway. The strong-minded Mrs. Babbage had paid for the 'whole inside' of the coach and considered it a great 'imposition' when she was expected to share the railway carriage with others. When they tried to enter she barred the way and so remained in possession. A year or two later she took them to Margate, where they read the novels of their father's school friend, Captain Marryat.

Charles seems to have taken no part whatsoever in bringing up his children, maintaining his bachelor establishment at 1 Dorset Street and concentrating exclusively on his own affairs, working on the machine, quarrelling with the Royal Society and Joseph Clement, writing, giving parties, going to parties, dining out. He slept very little, being constantly disturbed by an unceasing anxiety to resume some train of thought which had occupied his mind during the day. He always placed beside his bed a lamp and writing materials.

In 1831 he published the twenty-one volumes of his famous *Specimens of Logarithmic Tables*, of which only a single copy was printed. The object was to ascertain by experiment the tints of papers and colours of ink least fatiguing to the eye. The work contained 151 various coloured papers and inks in light and dark blue, light and dark green, olive, yellow, light and dark red, purple and black. This work is still of great interest, and is in the Crawford Library at the Royal Observatory, Edinburgh.

What is nowadays regarded as a pioneer work on operational research, *Economy of Manufactures*, came out in 1832. The main theme was the division of labour, applied to mental as well as to mechanical operations. The book soon went into a second edition and has since been reprinted many times and translated into several languages.

In order to gather material for it he had visited numerous factories and workshops on the Continent as well as in England. He usually stayed at hostelries for commercial travellers, which was not only cheaper but also more productive of the information he sought. Once, in Sheffield, to his secret delight, he was eventually located by one of Lord Fitzwilliam's grooms, who had made a fruitless search of the hotels. Charles, nothing loath, left his humble lodging to spend a very pleasant week at Wentworth Woodhouse.

The British Association had been recently founded by Sir David Brewster, Sir John Robison and the Rev. William Vernon Harcourt, Charles being a trustee for six years, 1832–8. The first two meetings were held at York and Oxford, and the third, at Cambridge, was attended by M. Quetelet, who had been sent by the Belgian Government. He was armed with a budget of statistics for which there was no place in any section. This gave Charles the idea of forming a statistical section, and his idea was eventually adopted. And this led, on 15th March

1834, to the formation of the Statistical Society of London, Charles becoming chairman.

Dr. Dionysius Lardner, who had a gift for making abstruse technical subjects comprehensible to the uninitiated, published his paper 'Babbage's Calculating Engines' in *The Edinburgh Review* in June 1834. This, together with his lectures on the subject, probably did more than anything else to make the difference engine known to a wide public. Lardner was indeed one of Charles Babbage's best advocates. He not only explained the machine itself and the difficulty and tediousness of compiling the numerous astronomical and nautical tables indispensable to a great maritime nation, but he also stressed the analogous case of the steam engine, the improvements to which alone occupied no fewer than twenty years of Watts' life and cost no less than £50,000.

Charles, who took a special delight in overcoming a difficulty for its own sake, would often, without apparent effort, and almost as a form of relaxation, turn aside from the complexities of Lagrange and Laplace to decipher secret writing or, like the Greek geometer Archytas, concentrate all his energies on constructing a toy or other trivial mechanical contrivance.

Ciphers had interested him since his schooldays, and he spent hours working on specimens submitted by his friends, displaying an amount of ingenuity, patience and perseverance that would have made him indispensable in the two world wars. He deciphered the letter of Abraham Sharpe, assistant to John Flamsteed, the first Astronomer Royal, to Mr. J. Crosthwait, on 2nd February 1721, published by Francis Baily in his life of Flamsteed.

On the 4th November of the same year, 1835, the Governor of the Bank of England requested his help in improving the methods of the Bank's printing and engraving establishment, and in the following year he was asked to serve on a committee to investigate the forgery of banknotes, at that time very prevalent, and to suggest means for its prevention. For his services on this committee he received a vote of thanks from the Governor and Company of the Bank—'an honour usually reserved for warriors and statesmen', he observed.

The same note of bitterness crept into his reference to the newly created post of Registrar-General of Births, Deaths and Marriages. Francis Baily and other friends suggested that he was specially qualified for this appointment, but on making enquiries he decided that it would be useless to apply, 'as the place was intended for the brother-in-law of a Secretary of State'.

Another of his interests was the new railway system, and he was at Liverpool for the opening of the Manchester and Liverpool Railway in 1830, when William Huskisson, Colonial Secretary and leader of the House of Commons, was killed.

In 1838 Charles was asked by his friend Mark Isambard Brunel and the directors of the Great Western Railway to investigate some of the difficulties and dangers of this new mode of travel. He therefore fitted up a second-class carriage with machinery of his own devising. He removed all the internal parts and through its base firm supports, attached to the framework below, passed up into the carriage itself, supporting a long table entirely independent of its motions.

'On this table slowly rolled sheets of paper, each a thousand feet long. Several inking pens traced curves on this paper, which expressed the following measures: (1) Force of traction. (2) Vertical shake of carriage at its middle. (3) Lateral ditto. (4) End ditto. (5, 6 and 7) The same shakes at the end of the carriage. (8) The curves described upon the earth by the centre of the frame of the carriage. (9) A chronometer marked half-seconds on the paper.'

About two miles of paper were thus covered in this dynamometer car, and the experiment cost him about £300, occupying about five months.

His experiments were often dangerous because it was sometimes necessary to attach his carriage to a public train to convey him to the point he wished to reach, frequently having to interrupt their course 'in order to run on to a siding to avoid a coming train'. The highest speed ever to be experienced by him was seventy-eight miles per hour on a train returning from Bristol.

One day he found Dr. Lardner making experiments, so

offered the services of himself and his son Herschel. Lardner's engine, travelling at known velocities, was drawing a series of trucks, these being detached independently at certain intervals. The object was to note the time taken before the truck came to a standstill. Charles's truck was detached and came to rest. He then noted a slight motion which he attributed to the high wind. It was very cold and having purchased three yards of coarse woollen cloth to serve as a wrap, he now unwound it and held it up as a sail. Gradually they acquired velocity and sailed across the Hanworth viaduct 'at a very fair pace'.

Through these railroad experiments he became acquainted with George Stephenson, but found him a taciturn companion.

His final conclusions were these:

1. Every engine should have mechanical self-registering means of recording its own velocity at every instant throughout its journey.

2. Between every engine and its train there should be interposed a dynamometer—that is, a powerful spring—to measure the force exerted by the engine.

3. The curve described by the centre of the engine itself upon the plane of railway should be recorded on paper.

These precautions, he thought, 'would add greatly to the security of railway travelling, because they would become the unerring record of facts, the incorruptible witnesses of the immediate antecedents of any catastrophe'.

Writing in 1864 he said that it was difficult to predict the railroads of the future, but a century hence he would no doubt have agreed wholeheartedly with Dr. Beeching's plans for rationalization. And his idea for a kind of horizontal escalator shows Dr. Beeching to be somewhat behind the times: 'Short and much frequented railways might be formed of a broad, continuous strap, always rolling on. At each station means must exist for taking up and putting down the passengers without stopping the rolling strap.' He also suggested light railways for exhibition buildings, including the new National Gallery. Had this been acted upon how many millions of weary, footsore people would have blessed his name!

Between railways and miracles there would seem to be a

considerable gap, but not so to the questing mind of Charles Babbage.

His views on religion are indeed of special interest, because he was totally lacking in the kind of arrogance that sometimes affects a certain type of scientific mind. He may have had little humility about his own achievements, but he had it to the ultimate degree in his views on his Maker, even though to the end of his life he could not bring himself to believe in the Athanasian Creed.

He published in May 1837 the *Ninth Bridgewater Treatise*, a second edition coming out in January 1838. The eighth had appeared in 1836, being the last to be commissioned as a result of a bequest of £8,000 by the Earl of Bridgewater for a series of works 'on the Power, Wisdom and Goodness of God, as manifested in the Creation'. The fund was administered by the Royal Society, acting on the advice of the Archbishop of Canterbury and the Bishop of London. Naturally, in view of the controversial nature of the subject, the awards failed to meet with general approval, Charles himself considering that one of the chief defects arose from the authors' not pursuing to its logical extent the argument of a great designing Power.

Many excellent religious persons had represented the Deity as perpetually interfering to alter for a time the laws He had previously ordained, thus by implication denying to Him the highest attribute of Omnipresence, he said. The difference engine could be employed to illustrate those laws, which might continue to operate for ages and then, after an enormous interval, to change into other different laws. This could be extended, he believed, to explain miracles. 'In much the same way as Sir James Jeans seemed to think of the Creator as a Mathematician, Babbage seems to have thought of Him as a Programmer', writes Dr. Bowden.

The workings of machinery ran parallel to those of intellect, said Charles. The engine might be so set that at definite periods, known only to its maker, a certain lever might become movable during the calculation then making. The result of moving it might be to cause the then existing law to be violated for one or more times, after which the original law would then resume its reign. The inventor might, of course, confide this fact to the person using it, who would thus be gifted with the power of prophecy if he foretold the event or of working a miracle at the proper time if he withheld his knowledge from those around until the moment of its taking place.

He believed that the works of the Creator afforded more convincing proofs of the existence of a supreme Being than any evidence transmitted through human testimony. And in support of this view cited the game of Russian scandal, in which A writes a tale, takes B into another room and communicates it to him. A then goes out and sends in C, to whom the tale is told by B. B goes out and sends in D, and so on until the tale has been transmitted through twelve educated and truthful witnesses. The twelfth then relates to the whole party the story he has just heard. Afterwards the original document is read, whereupon it is invariably found that the wit, and even the crux, is gone, because, as Charles pointed out, considerable training is necessary to become an accurate witness of facts, and no two persons, no matter how well trained, ever express in the same words the facts both have observed.

He considered the great virtue in man to be *truth*—that is, the constant application of the same word to the same thing. And the true value of the Christian religion rested, he said, not upon speculative views of the Creator, which must necessarily be different in each individual, according to the extent of the knowledge of the finite being, who employed his own feeble powers in contemplating the infinite; it rested on those doctrines of kindness and benevolence which that religion claimed and enforced, not merely in favour of man himself, but of every creature susceptible of pain or happiness.

Memory seemed to Charles to be the only faculty which must of necessity be preserved in order to render a future existence possible. 'If memory be absolutely destroyed, our personal identity is lost.' Although he did not mention the word, he seems also to have believed in reincarnation, for he said that in a future state we might perhaps awake to the recollection that we had existed not in one former state, but in many, and that the then state of existence and our rewards and punishments might be the consequence of our conduct in those former ages.

He thought it would be very interesting if naturalists could devise some means of showing that the dragonfly in its three stages—a grub beneath the soil, an animal living in the water, and that of a flying insect—had in the last stage any memory of its existence in its first.

There was a yet more difficult question: through his senses man possessed five sources of knowledge. He proudly thought of himself as the highest work of God; but it was quite *possible* that he might be the very lowest. If other animals possessed senses of a different nature from ours it could scarcely be possible that we could ever be aware of the fact. Yet those animals, having other sources of information and of pleasure, might, though despised by us, yet enjoy a corporeal as well as an intellectual existence far higher than our own.

15

Design for a 'Brain'

*

WHILE deprived of his tools and drawings by Joseph Clement, Charles Babbage, in addition to his other multifarious activities, had been speculating on the possibility of constructing a machine based upon an entirely different principle from that of the difference engine, by means of which he believed that he could secure an unlimited power over the most complicated operations of arithmetic. For this a mechanical means of controlling the operations of the machine and of presenting numbers to it in a form it could assimilate was of vital importance. This means was already available in Jacquard's punched cards.

It was in 1801 that Joseph-Marie Jacquard introduced the loom which bears his name and which is still in use in the textile industries. The pattern was painted on point, or rule, paper, from which pattern cards were cut—one card for each pick of weft throughout the design. A punched hole in the card corresponded to a lifted thread and a blank to a depressed thread; in other words, it anticipated the zero and one, the on/off, the yes/no, the binary system, of the modern electronic digital computer.

Simplification now assumed great importance, said Buxton, for if this could be carried out it was difficult to foresee or estimate the results which might be achieved. In the difference engine such simplification affected only about 120 similar parts, whereas in the analytical engine, as the inventor had named his new conception, it would affect a great many thousands. The difference engine might be constructed with more or less advantage by employing various mechanical means for the operation of addition, whereas the new analytical engine could not *exist* without inventing for it a method of mechanical addition of the utmost simplicity. If these ideas were verified, thought Charles Babbage, it might be that the new engine would execute more rapidly the operations for which the difference engine had been specially constructed.

This problem of possible obsolescence, familiar to all engineers, greatly exercised his mind, but, finally, he decided that it was his duty to inform the Government. He therefore sought an interview with the Prime Minister, now Lord Melbourne, but before anything could be done the administration went out of office. A new Government being formed, his friend the Duke of Wellington holding the seals of office until Sir Robert Peel's return from Italy, Charles applied in December 1834 for an interview, but the Duke, doubtless harassed by affairs of state, asked for an explanation in writing.

Accordingly Charles wrote, touching on a number of questions before coming to the analytical engine, such questions as whether the Government wished him to continue the construction of the difference engine either in the hands of Clement or any alternative engineer; whether they wished to substitute someone other than himself to superintend the completion of the machine; or whether, on the other hand, the Government wished to give up the undertaking altogether. He then explained the circumstances which had led him to the invention of the analytical engine, adding that this did not supersede the difference engine but greatly increased its utility. The Duke, however, relinquished the seals of office on Peel's return and the matter was again indefinitely postponed.

Meanwhile, at the end of 1835 the draughtsman, hitherto employed by Charles at his own expense and responsible for much of the work on both the difference engine and the analytical engine, was offered a much higher salary to go abroad. As he was indispensable, Charles had to pay him what he asked.

It was not until 14th January 1836 that he received a

reply to his letter to the Duke of Wellington. It came from the then Chancellor of the Exchequer, Thomas Spring Rice, afterwards first Baron Monteagle, who, like F. J. Robinson in 1823, utterly misunderstood the tenor of his communication, remarking that the inference to be drawn from it was that Mr. Babbage, having invented a new machine of far greater powers than the former one, wished to know whether the Government would undertake to defray the expense of the new engine. He then explained why he felt compelled to look for the completion of the difference engine before he could propose to Parliament the question of considering the second, and he intended to refer to the Royal Society for their opinion.

Charles Babbage realized at once that he had again failed to communicate the impression he intended or to make his views understood. Even after all these years he did not speak the same language as the Establishment or they his. His first object, when applying to Lord Melbourne, had been to raise the question whether his new discoveries might not ultimately supersede the work already executed and, secondly, to point out a possible arrangement whereby great expense might be spared in the construction of the difference engine. He had not in any way asked or inferred that the Government should defray the cost of building the analytical engine.

Still firmly convinced that he had only done his duty in informing the Government of his new discoveries, he wrote to the Chancellor on 29th January 1836 saying that on re-examining his own statement to Lord Melbourne he did not see that it contained any request to the Government to take up the new analytical engine. In a separate statement he explained that the analytical engine was not only capable of accomplishing all those complicated calculations peculiar to the difference engine, but could do it in less time and to a greater extent. In fact, he added (now being certain of what he said), it completely superseded the difference engine.

All the elements of the analytical engine were essentially different from those of the difference engine; the mechanical simplicity to which they had been reduced was such that it would probably cost more to finish the old difference engine on its original plan than to construct a new difference engine with the simplified elements.

'The fact of a *new* superseding an *old* machine in a very few years is one of constant occurrence in our manufactories,' he said, 'and instances might be pointed out in which the advance of invention has been so rapid, and the demand for machinery so great, that half-finished machines have been thrown aside as useless before their completion.'

It was now nearly fourteen years since he undertook for the Government to superintend the construction of the difference engine, he continued. During nearly five years its construction had been absolutely stopped, and instead of being employed in overcoming the physical impediments he had been harassed by what might be called the moral difficulties of the question. It was painful to reflect that in the time so employed the first difference engine might under more favourable circumstances have been completed.

'In making this report I wish distinctly to state that I do not entertain the slightest doubt of the success of the difference engine; *nor do I intend it as any application to finish the one, or to construct the other*, but I make it from a conviction that the information it contains ought to be communicated to those who must decide the question relative to the difference engine.'

For nearly two years Charles daily awaited a reply, but none came, in spite of personal applications and through the co-operation of his friends. Bitterly he reflected that for fourteen years he had been engaged upon a task which he had genuinely believed could not occupy him for more than two or three years during which he had abandoned other important pursuits. His plans and ambitions had become embarrassed or disappointed, his time sacrificed and his leisure utterly destroyed. Was this state of affairs to continue indefinitely? he asked himself.

At last, wearied and frustrated beyond endurance, he decided to make one final attempt to obtain some decision, and wrote to Lord Melbourne, as first Lord of the Treasury, on 26th July 1838, bluntly stating that if difficulties had arisen out of the obsolescence of the difference engine the blame lay with the Government, and had arisen entirely from that delay which for years he had complained of and against which he had never ceased to remonstrate. All he now asked, and for the last time, was not an act of grace but a right which could not be refused—he required a decision.

The reply, when it came, was based on the original misunderstanding, the Chancellor of the Exchequer enquiring whether he wished steps to be taken for the completion of the old, or for the construction of a new, machine, and what did he consider these projects would cost.

Charles suspected, rightly or wrongly, that this was an attempt to place him in a false position, and he determined not to fall into the trap. When he replied, on 21st October, he said categorically that he had no intention of applying to construct a new machine, and as to the question of cost, not being a professional engineer, and his past experience having taught him not to rely upon his own judgement in such matters, he would be very reluctant to offer any opinion upon the subject. In conclusion he solicited a categorical answer to the following question: whether the Government required him to superintend the completion of the difference engine, which had been suspended during the last five years, according to the original plan and principles; or whether they intended to discontinue it altogether.

No further communication took place for some considerable time, and Charles, fatigued and harassed by delay, and surmising from the studied reticence of the Government their real intentions, went off to Italy for a meeting of philosophers.

16

Triumph at Turin

*

A PRESSING invitation had come from his friend Baron Plana, one of the first mathematicians in Europe, who remarked that he had made many anxious enquiries about the analytical engine and believed that he was correct in saying: 'Hitherto the *legislative* department of our analysis has been all powerful—the *executive* all feeble. Your engine seems to give us the same control over the executive which we have hitherto only possessed over the legislative department.'

Charles Babbage was delighted by this 'exact pre-vision of its powers', and, considering the limited amount of information available, very much surprised. Collecting drawings, models and notations, he therefore left happily for Turin, and there explained the principles of the engine to some of Italy's greatest mathematicians and engineers, including Plana himself, Professor Mosotti, L. F. Menabrea and Plantamour.

Plana had intended to take notes in order to write a paper, but, owing to the demands on his time, handed over the task to Menabrea, who, although a younger man, was already well known as a profound analyst. The latter, who was to become one of Garibaldi's generals and to play a considerable part in the unification of Italy, eventually becoming Prime Minister, at once grasped the principles of the machine and was to publish his 'lucid and admirable description' (*vide* Charles Babbage) in the *Bibliothèque Universelle de Genève* in October 1842. He thus became the first to make these principles known to the public. Mathematically speaking, then, unlike his own country, Italy once more took Charles Babbage to its heart. There he received all the understanding, respect and homage which he considered, rightly, to be his due.

In his account of his reception at the little court of the King of Sardinia, however, he once again revealed the childish side to his character, the side that revelled in decorations and in medals, in ribbons and in stars. On enquiring when there would be a levee he learned that King Charles Albert was aware of his arrival and would receive him at a private audience. Court dress was therefore unnecessary, he was told, he could wear plain clothes. Greatly disappointed by this Charles told General de Salluce, tutor to the two princes, that he thought it would be most respectful to wear the same dress he had worn a few days before leaving England, 'when I had the honour of being invited to the first party given by a subject to my own sovereign'. This was a *dejeuné* at Wimbledon Park, the residence of the Duke of Somerset, for the young Queen Victoria.

The King was intensely shy and reserved, and, although having suffered from the same affliction in youth, Charles found it very hard going until he happened to mention the electric telegraph, when the King asked him for what purposes it would become useful. Charles Babbage replied that probably by this means H.M. Fleet might receive warning of coming storms, and he gave as an example a storm which occurred shortly before he left England. The damage at Liverpool was very great, and at Glasgow immense. 'It arose from the over-lapping of two circular whirlwinds, one of them coming up from the Atlantic bodily at the rate of twenty miles an hour, in a north-westerly direction, to Glasgow, where they coalesced and destroyed property to the value of half a million sterling.' Electric communication between Genoa and other places, he explained, would have given the people of Glasgow twenty-four hours' notice of the arrival of these storms and enabled them to take effective measures for the security of much of their shipping.

When the audience ended the King held out his hand, and Charles might well have kissed it, but fortunately had taken the precaution of finding out the correct procedure—the ceremony of kissing hands took place only when a native subject was appointed to high office—the King wished to do him the honour of shaking hands in the English fashion.

At the opera that evening an Italian friend who had been dining at the palace said: 'What an extraordinary person you are! You have perfectly fascinated our King, who has done nothing but talk of you and the things you have told him during the whole of dinner-time.'

Charles had brought several models and scientific and mechanical instruments and showed them to the princes, aged seventeen and eighteen. He had hoped the Queen would be present, for she was a sister of Leopold II, Grand Duke of Tuscany, from whom he had received much kindness in 1828, but the lord-in-waiting would have had to disturb the King at a council meeting to ask his permission, and to this the Queen would not consent.

On the journey out Charles had passed through Lyons, in order to examine the silk manufacture, and especially to see the loom on which 'that admirable specimen of fine art, the portrait of Jacquard, was woven'. One copy he already possessed, but, although they were not usually for sale, he was allowed to purchase another. This he suggested giving to the Queen, whereupon General de Salluce looked extremely grave and said: 'I will take the King's pleasure on the subject.'

The King's pleasure was to grant another audience. The portrait was enclosed in a large cartoon case, and having removed it Charles showed it to the King, who approved its presentation to Her Majesty. Charles was replacing it when a multitude of sheets of silver paper flew out. He tried to catch them, the King tried, but to no avail. Soon both the King and Charles Babbage were grovelling on their knees. 'I suddenly felt an obstacle presented to my right foot. On looking round I perceived that the heel of royalty had come into contact with the toe of philosophy. A comic yet kindly smile beamed upon the countenance of the King, whilst an irrepressible but not irreverent one, lightened up my own.'

The King's reserve being thus completely broken down, they began to talk, one subject being wine-making. Having no first-hand experience of it, Charles gladly accepted an invitation to examine the vintage at Raconigi, a royal estate about twelve miles from Turin. Accompanied by one of the officers of the household, he was driven in one of the royal carriages through beautiful country. On their return a dragoon accompanied the carriage. Charles was much gratified by this escort, but was nevertheless 'uncomfortable at the idea of having a man galloping after our carriage for ten miles. I therefore appealed to my friend to suspend this unnecessary loss of *vis viva*. With some reluctance the dragoon was exempted from further attendance upon the philosopher.'

An Italian friend later remarked: 'The King has done three things for you, which are very unusual—he has shaken hands with you, he has asked you to sit down at an audience, he has permitted you to make a present to the Queen. This last is the rarest of all.'

At a final audience Charles Babbage said that he would take the mail to Geneva because it crossed that remarkable suspension bridge the Pont Charles Albert. This, named after the King, was 600 "French feet" long, the same distance as the depth of the chasm over which it was suspended. Whereupon, to Charles's immense gratification, the King immediately opened a drawer and, withdrawing a small bronze medal, struck to celebrate the opening of the bridge, presented it to him.

Two days later Charles left for Geneva. On approaching the bridge the scene was 'singularly grand'. The bridge could be seen quite clearly one moment, the next it would disappear in the mist. 'It really seemed like a bridge springing from a lofty cliff spanning the sea beneath and suspended on the distant clouds', he wrote with poetic feeling.

On arrival at Annecy he was not feeling well, so his companion suggested that as the mail would wait forty-five minutes he should get into bed and take some refreshment. The suggestion was gratefully received, and he was called in due time for the mail.

His reflections on this visit to Turin were exceptionally interesting. He could not understand why he had received such a favourable reception from the King. It could not be the analytical engine, he mused. A sovereign, he went on, could not have a real friend, or, if he had, know it. On the other hand, he (Charles) had never stated more than he really knew. This was, he believed, a very unusual practice in courts of every kind. And when it happened to be obviously sincere it commanded great influence. And then, at the end, the characteristic note of bitterness crept in: 'There might be yet another reason: it was well known that I had nothing to ask for—to expect—or to desire.'

17

Interview with Peel

*

*F*ORTIFIED by his reception in Italy, Charles Babbage, now aged fifty, decided on his return to London in November 1841 to reopen negotiations with the Government, Sir Robert Peel being now Prime Minister. In order, as he hoped, to clarify matters, he furnished a detailed statement of what had occurred, together with a letter in which he said:

'Of course when I undertook to give the invention of the calculating engine to the Government, and to superintend its construction, there must have been an implied understanding that I should carry it on to its termination. I entered upon that undertaking believing that *two*, or at the utmost *three*, years would complete it. The better part of my life has now been spent on that machine, and no progress whatever having been made since 1834, that undertaking may possibly be considered by the Government as still subsisting, I am therefore naturally very anxious that this state of uncertainty should be put an end to as soon as possible.'

Another year passed, in which Peel conferred with Henry Goulburn, who was again Chancellor, and with Professor, now Sir, George Airy, Astronomer Royal. The latter wrote in his diary: 'On September 15th Mr. Goulburn . . . asked my opinion on the utility of Babbage's calculating machine, and the propriety of expending further sums of money on it. I replied, entering fully into the matter, and giving my opinion that it was worthless.'

Accordingly, on 4th November 1842, the Chancellor wrote to Charles Babbage saying that both Sir Robert and himself regretted the necessity of abandoning the completion of a machine on which so much scientific labour had been bestowed. The expense necessary for rendering it either satisfactory to Mr. Babbage or generally useful appeared on the lowest calculation so far to exceed what they should be justified in incurring, that they considered themselves as having no other alternative. It was hoped that by the Government's abandoning all claim to the machine as already constructed, and placing it entirely at Mr. Babbage's disposal, he might in some degree be assisted in his future exertions in the cause of science.

The verdict, though not unexpected, still came as a shock. At this time the whole of the plans for the complete engine had been laid down, occupying ninety boxes, each plan being numbered and indexed, and the whole of the contents carefully distinguished and classified. The drawings represented the machine as capable of containing any numbers on the table axis, and on each of the six axes for the differences which did not extend beyond twenty places of figures. All the principles necessary for the completion of the engine were recorded on these plans, so that it would have been quite possible to make them available for the purposes of the engineer. And a part of the machine had been put together in 1833.

On the 6th of the same month Charles replied, declining to accept the finished part of the machine. A few days later he obtained an interview with Peel; and, determined not to repeat the error of his interview with F. J. Robinson in 1823, recorded his own minutes of what transpired. Even today, over a century later, the reader senses the pain and anguish, the feeling of gross injustice, the quivering, sensitive lip, the brimming eye. On the other hand, there was Peel—of whom the Duke of Wellington said: 'I never knew a man in whose truth and justice I had more lively confidence'—Peel, aware only of the fact that the machine was still unfinished. But he listened in silence to what Charles had to say.

Having delivered the original invention to the Government, and superintended its construction, he had demonstrated the possibility of the undertaking by the completion of an important part of it, he said, and urged upon Sir Robert that failure to complete the whole engine was not his fault. It was solely and entirely the fault of the Government, and he submitted that in common justice and fair dealing he had some claims to their consideration.

He further urged upon the Prime Minister the losses in time and money which had been sustained by the harassing procrastination and protracted delays of the Government together with the annoyance to which he had been incessantly exposed by the prevailing belief in the public mind that he had been rewarded for his time and labour by grants from the public purse. He deeply resented it, and hoped that Sir Robert Peel would see the necessity of refuting this 'vulgar error' by some public act of the Government.

With the Astronomer Royal in mind, he then 'gently hinted' that Sir Robert's views upon the merits of the difference engine must have been formed from some advice or suggestions of some adept, or person presumed to be acquainted with such matters.

'You, Sir Robert, cannot be supposed, especially in the teeth of the very eminent persons whose opinions have been recorded in its favour, to take upon yourself the responsibility of reversing their deliberate judgement. I, of course, have no desire that you should tell me the name or names of any individuals who might or might not have other motives than the promotion of justice and the public weal; but anonymous advisers never inspire confidence. I have no desire that you should raise the veil which shrouds the sources of your counsel. I do not ask for exposure. I only *wish you to understand* the state of my own conviction on the subject. I have no desire to encroach upon your discretion, nor importunately pry into a state secret, if such there be. Of course a communication which involves the rights of another person cannot have been made under any contract of confidence.'

Peel made no reply to this, so that Charles's suspicions about Airy were neither confirmed nor denied.

He then turned to the next subject, the importance of the analytical engine, stating his own opinion (fully justified in the event) that in the future scientific history of their day it would probably form a marked epoch, and that much depended upon the result of this interview. The difference engine, he added, was capable of application only to one limited part of the science (although that part was certainly of great importance, and capable of more immediate practical application than any other); but the analytical engine embraced the whole science. It was, in fact, already invented, and it exceeded any hopes he had ever entertained respecting the powers of applying machinery to science.

Having delivered himself of these preliminaries, he now came to the point on which he had sought the interview, saying that at an early period of life he had given up the prospect of succeeding his father in a lucrative profession, that of a banker in the City, in order to devote himself to science.

In following out that pursuit he had invented the difference engine. The Government in 1823 wished that such a machine should be constructed. At their desire he had undertaken the construction of it for them, and during twelve years he had devoted, amidst many difficulties, his whole time and energy to that object. Circumstances over which he had no control caused what was then thought to be a temporary cessation.

During this interval he had been examining other combinations of machinery, and had opened out views which seemed likely to have the most important bearings upon the machine then constructing. When new arrangements were made, and the Government wished the work to be resumed, he thought it would be improper to withhold from them the knowledge thus acquired.

He communicated this knowledge, but no decision was arrived at by the Government. As time advanced, those views became gradually more clear and distinct, and ultimately it appeared that it would be both a *shorter* and *more economical* course to throw aside all that had been done and to make a new difference engine, using for it some of the more simple contrivances which he had invented for the analytical engine. Finding still that the Government, after repeated applications, came to no decision, he confined his subsequent applications to the simple question: whether they intended to call on him

to complete the old difference engine or to abandon it altogether.

'Year after year passed, in which I was kept in the most
harassing state of uncertainty. Now after nine years I have
just received notice of the intention of the Government altogether to abandon the engine. During that time I have myself
expended a large sum of money, and the public have constantly accused me of having myself received that money which
Government has paid to the workmen. On the grounds of the
great pecuniary and personal sacrifices which I have made,
and on the expectations I might reasonably have entertained
upon the completion of such a machine, which have now been
by your decision abandoned, I thought that the services I had
rendered ought not to be utterly unrequited and unrewarded.'

Up to this point the Prime Minister seems to have kept silence;
but then Charles, in his bitterness, lost face and dignity by
saying that while he had been thus exerting himself in advancing
science many others pursuing the same career had been rewarded
by the Government for their labours, while he was made the
marked exception. Peel's immediate retort was to refer to the
pensions given to science and literature amounting to only
£1,200 each year. Charles replied that although he partially
alluded to them, there were other means and occasions by
which science was rewarded, remarking that he would mention
half a dozen names not unknown to the Prime Minister, leaving
him to put the amount of income derived by them, which the
other probably knew better than he did. On these grounds he
thought that he had some claim to the consideration of the
Government.

Sir Robert, enraged, flatly denied that either of these
claims entitled him to any consideration, revealing his own
ignorance of the main issue by observing that Charles had
rendered the difference engine useless by inventing a better.
To this Charles Babbage replied that if finished it would be
more than he had promised, and that although it was undoubtedly superseded by better machinery yet he had never
stated that it was useless.

The general fact of machinery's being superseded in several

great branches of manufacture after a few years was perfectly well known.

He then enlarged on the anxiety which he had suffered, and the vexation of finding that the public believed he had profited by the money expended. This belief was so prevalent, he said, that several of his intimate friends had asked if it were not true, and he had even met with it on the hustings at Finsbury. To this the Prime Minister retorted coldly: 'You are too sensitive to such attacks. Men of sense never care for them.'

Cruelly wounded by this, and thinking of the fate of Sir Samuel Romilly, law reformer and Solicitor General to the administration of 'All the Talents', who committed suicide on his wife's death, and of Samuel Whitbread, who also took his own life, he looked Peel straight in the face, saying very seriously and deliberately:

'You must, Sir Robert Peel, in your own experience of public life, have frequently observed that the best heads, and highest order of minds, are often the most susceptible of annoyance from the injustice or ingratitude of the public.'

Peel seemed to admit this, but Charles was not sure that the names of Romilly, Whitbread and others occurred to him.

With respect to the other ground of claim that, compared with other men of science, he had been utterly neglected, Peel 'tried rather artfully' to interpret Charles's statement as meaning to put himself in competition for the places held by others. He had begun by denying this expressly, and repeated that they were all men eminent in science, and that, not wishing to disparage them in the slightest degree, he yet had a right to be considered as belonging to that class.

Sir Robert replied that most of them were professional rewards. This Charles at once denied, saying that it was perfectly well known that they were not given for professional services; for although eminent in science they had not any of them *ever done* anything to distinguish them professionally.

'Sir R. Peel seemed excessively angry and annoyed during the whole interview, but more particularly when I knocked over, with some vivacity, his argument about *professional* service. He then proceeded to attempt humbug, saying that the Institutions of the country &c. admitted of certain places being given to certain professions for services not exactly professional and so on.

'I listened to all his statement looking him steadfastly in the face. When he got aground I still retained my view of him, as if expecting at least some argument would be produced. This position of course was far from agreeable, and certainly not very dignified for a Prime Minister.

'Finding Sir R. Peel unwilling to admit that I had any claim, I merely remarked that I considered myself as having been treated with great injustice, but that as he seemed to be of a different opinion, I could not help myself, on which I got up and wished him good morning.'

The result of this interview was in every respect, as Buxton says in a masterly understatement, most unsatisfactory. Charles Babbage had previously determined to point out two courses to the Government by either of which he thought it probable that not only a difference engine but even the analytical engine might in a few years be completed. But the position assumed by Peel, and the state of his information on the subject, precluded the possibility of adopting that course and prevented his alluding to those plans.

In spite of all, however, Peel subsequently offered Charles a baronetcy, which he declined, ostensibly on the ground that his eldest son Herschel (of whose wife, incidentally, he disapproved) and not his youngest son Henry, who had become closely associated with him in his work, would succeed. The real reason may have been quite different and similar to the contemptuous reply he made when Henry Brougham in 1830 was deputed to sound him on the subject of knighthood. Peel also admitted in the House of Commons in March 1843 that Charles Babbage gave his services gratuitously and that from first to last he had derived no emolument whatsoever from the Government.

From 1842 until 1848, when he finally mastered the theory, Charles Babbage devoted himself almost exclusively to the construction of the analytical engine, discovering from time to time the principles upon which its multifarious powers and unlimited capabilities depended. Deprived of all financial aid from the Government, he persevered at his own expense, employing draughtsmen and workmen, maintaining in his own house the investigations and experiments necessary to accomplish his supreme work of genius.

Part Three
(1842–1852)

*

Magis verit animorum quam corporum conjugiam (The wedlock of minds will be greater than that of bodies).

ERASMUS, *Procus et Puella*

Let me not to the marriage of true minds
Admit impediments

WILLIAM SHAKESPEARE, *Sonnets*, No. CXVI

18

Foreign Mathematician: English Countess

*

L. F. MENABREA's paper on the analytical engine appeared in French in the *Bibliothèque Universelle de Genève* in October 1842. Soon afterwards the Countess of Lovelace told Charles Babbage that she had translated it for Taylor's *Scientific Memoirs*. He asked why she had not written an original paper. The thought had not occurred to her, she replied. He then suggested that she should add some notes to Menabrea's memoir. The idea was at once adopted. These notes extended to about three times the length of the original paper. She was twenty-seven years old.

'These memoirs, taken together,' said Charles Babbage, 'furnish, to those who are capable of understanding the reasoning, a complete demonstration that the whole of the developments and operations of analysis are now capable of being executed by machinery.'

The translation and notes were to evoke a sneering remark from Richard Sheepshanks to the effect that Charles Babbage was too lazy to write about his own machine and had left it to a foreign mathematician and an English countess to do it for him. In fact, he had something better to do, and could not have had more able or accomplished expositors; and in his long friendship with Lady Lovelace, which culminated only with her tragic death, he found true sympathy and understanding of his work and genius. For the next ten years his life was dominated by this remarkable young woman.

In spite of the endless volumes which have been written about Lord Byron little has been known or said about his only legitimate child. The Honourable Augusta Ada Byron was born in London, at 13 Piccadilly Terrace, facing the Green Park, on 10th December 1815, six months after the Battle of Waterloo, and was therefore about the same age as Charles Babbage's only daughter, Georgiana. 'Her name', said Byron, on 5th January 1816, 'is Augusta *Ada*.' He had looked up the family pedigree and found the name Ada—that of Charlemagne's sister, he noted—in the reign of King John. Augusta was from his half-sister, the Hon. Mrs. Augusta Leigh, with whom he had had incestuous relations.

The child was only a few months old when her parents separated and Byron left England for ever, to see neither his wife nor his daughter again. She was made a Ward in Chancery, and in his anger and bitterness Byron was to open the third canto of *Childe Harold* with the now famous lines:

'Is thy face like thy mother's, my fair child!
Ada! sole daughter of my house and heart?
When last I saw thy young blue eyes they smiled,
And then we parted—not as now we part
But with a hope.'

She was nearly four years old when her father requested that she should be taught Italian and 'pray let her be musical if she has a turn that way'. She had a turn that way—growing up to become a good linguist and to play several instruments, especially the violin, with professional skill. Four years later her father's stormy life ended at Missolonghi. As he lay dying he groaned: 'Oh, my poor dear child!—my dear Ada! my God, could I but have seen her!' And he instructed Fletcher, his valet, to give her his blessing.

By the time she was fifteen she was showing her extraordinary talent for mathematics, which she inherited from her mother, the former Miss Annabella Milbanke, and had already taught herself part of Paisley's *Geometry*. Her first known association with Charles Babbage, who knew Lady Byron well, dates from this time. She wrote in Greek characters what appeared to be a begging letter from three sisters; it was 'bad in spelling, bad in grammar—ancient and modern words', said Henry Babbage. Dated 7th December 1831, the sheet of paper was found among his father's papers, enclosed in an envelope on which she had written: 'A piece of humbug for Mr. Babbage's approval, by Lady L. To be carefully studied.'

In May 1833 she was presented at court. When her second season was over she was taken on a factory tour, meanwhile studying astronomy. It is pleasant to know that her enjoyment on seeing the machinery was equalled by her love of dancing. Overcoming her own intense dislike of any kind of frivolity, Lady Byron then took her to Doncaster for the races, so that she might see and judge worldly pleasures for herself. This particular pleasure, as her mother was to learn to her sorrow, Ada Byron was to like only too well. Apart from Doncaster races, her greatest delight in 1834 was to go to the Mechanics' Institute to hear the first of Dr. Dionysius Lardner's lectures on the difference engine.

She paid frequent visits to Dorset Street, often with Mary Somerville, though sometimes with Mrs. De Morgan. Of one of these visits Mrs. De Morgan said: 'While the rest of the party gazed at this beautiful instrument [the difference engine] with the same sort of expression and feeling that some savages are said to have shown on first seeing a looking glass or hearing a gun, Miss Byron, young as she was, understood its working and saw the great beauty of the invention.' On this Dr. Bowden comments ironically: 'It is remarkable that the attitude of the average man to a computing machine should have changed so little in a hundred years.'

This quality of comprehension had a terrific impact on Charles Babbage, who was accustomed to being asked the silliest questions, such as: 'Pray, Mr. Babbage, if you put into the machine wrong figures, will the right answer come out?' And: 'Please explain, in two words, the principle of the machine.' To which Charles says that he *could* have answered in four words, if his interlocutor had known anything about mathematics—the method of differences; or in six characters:

$$\Delta^r u_x = 0.$$

Ada Byron made a striking change from the wall of ignorance, indifference and complacency by which he was encompassed. Young as she was, and surrounded by the Byronic aura and legend, it was her brain that earned a respect from the host at his Saturday evening parties which most of his guests failed to inspire. There was no need to show her the silver lady, a recent acquisition, one of the two automata which he had found so captivating in childhood, now placed under a glass case on a pedestal in his drawing-room, his 'fair friends' assisting in dressing her and 'attending the toilette of their rival syren'.

The girl, indifferent to the automaton, was entranced by the machine. There is no other word for it. And, although it is axiomatic that nothing draws people together so much as a common interest, it is possible that she also found in Charles Babbage a substitute for the father she had never known.

There were strong associations with that father. Here was Charles Babbage aiming to mechanize brainwork while Lord Byron, as she must have known, had been much concerned with the Luddites, who wished to stop the mechanization of manual work. The frame-breaking movement had, in fact, started at Nottingham. After spending the Christmas of 1811 at Newstead Abbey, Byron spoke of 'nightly outrage and daily depredation'. He was twenty-four when he made his maiden speech in the House of Lords on 27th February 1812. The subject was the Bill making frame-breaking a capital offence. And from Venice, in 1816, he wrote to Thomas Moore: 'Are you near the Luddites? By the Lord! if there's a row, I'll be among ye! How go on the weavers—the breakers of frames—the Lutherans of politics—the reformers?' His daughter, no doubt, was familiar with the 'Song for the Luddites':

'As the liberty lads o'er the sea
Bought their freedom, and cheaply with blood,
So we, boys, we
Will *die* fighting or live *free*,
And down with all kings but King Ludd!'

There was yet another association. Six years after Byron's maiden speech, and six years after Charles Babbage, the twenty-one-year-old Cambridge undergraduate, first thought about working out logarithmic tables by machine, twenty-one-year-old Mary Wollstonecraft Shelley, wife of the poet, published *Frankenstein*. Byron was with Shelley and his wife on the shores of the Lake of Geneva when it was decided that each should write a ghost story. All started, but Mary Shelley was the only one to finish—she made her hero, Victor Frankenstein, succeed in devising a synthetic man, or, to use a term which came into general use some 125 years later with Karel Čapek's play *R.U.R.*, a robot.

Ada Byron was nineteen when, in 1835, she married William, eighth Baron King, created first Earl of Lovelace in 1838, who was ten years her elder. He was a good-natured and kindly man, and after the marriage Charles Babbage was to become a constant visitor to his town house in St. James's Square (afterwards in Great Cumberland Place) and to his country seats, Ockham Park, near Weybridge, and Ashley Combe in Somerset.

In spite of still being 'supervised' by her mother, who dominated Lord King, Lady King (as she was known for the first three years of her married life) flowered into a most remarkable woman, whose character and talents were justly summarized by Albany Fonblanque, editor of *The Examiner*, who knew her well. She was thoroughly original, he said, and her genius, 'for genius she possessed, was not poetic, but metaphysical and mathematical, her mind having been in the constant practice of investigation, and this with vigorous exactness. With an understanding thoroughly masculine in solidity, grasp and firmness, Lady Lovelace had all the delicacies of the most refined female character. Her manners, her tastes, her accomplishments, in many of which, music especially, she was a proficient, were feminine in the nicest sense of the word; and the superficial observer would never have divined the strength and the knowledge that lay hidden under the womanly graces. Proportionate to her distaste for the frivolous and commonplace was her enjoyment of true intellectual society, and eagerly she sought the acquaintance of all who were distinguished in science, art and literature'.

She was pretty, dark-haired and graceful, and inherited her father's lovely speaking voice. She was also small, slight and delicate and Charles always alluded to her as the 'lady fairy'.

Among her many gifts was the art of letter-writing, which she inherited from her father, one of the best letter-writers in the English language. The long series which she wrote to Charles Babbage not only throws new light on her translation of Menabrea's paper but also reveals a different side to his character, gallant but correct, playful and utterly devoted.

The first was dated Ockham Park, 18th January 1836. She was expecting her first child, and thanked him for some minerals which had been sent on from St. James's Square. 'I hope I shall also find courage enough to take to pieces one of the wooden crosses, though even with the other before me I doubt if I have the ingenuity to put it together again.' She added that she had quantities of formulae to work out and had destroyed a good deal of paper.

Lord King then took up the pen, asking Charles, on 4th February, to dine at Lady Byron's at Fordhook, and on 27th March suggesting that he should 'let the machine keep the passover, and come yourself to keep yours with us, arriving the day before Good Friday'. Lady King was anxious for him to come, not wholly from disinterested motives, 'as she has a set of questions to be asked'.

In May Lord King announced that his wife had given birth to 'a lusty, stout little fellow', and that she had abandoned hope of being able to see the eclipse. The 'little fellow' was Byron, later Viscount Ockham. Two years later, on 2nd March 1838, she herself wrote, referring to the birth of a daughter, afterwards Lady Anne King, who was to marry Wilfred Scawen Blunt and to become a distinguished Arabic scholar, and, with him, co-founder of the world-famous Crabbett stud of Arab horses.

'You may possibly have heard of the very tedious and suffering illness which has occupied so many months, since a Miss King has been added to our family.

'Though I am now to all appearances perfectly well again,

and am in fact most wonderfully improved, yet I am still far from being really strong. But for these untoward circumstances, Lord King or I myself should probably have written to you long ago and have strongly urged a visit or visits to Ockham.'

She also thanked Charles for a copy of the new edition of the *Ninth Bridgewater Treatise*, which may have had considerable influence in forming her taste for metaphysics.

On 16th March 1839 she invited him to Ockham for Easter, saying that Lady Byron was with them and would be glad to see him. He replied on the 23rd of that month.

Dear Lady Lovelace,

I have delayed a few days to answer your very kind invitation as I had an unarranged promise to spend a few days with the Duke of Somerset which is now fixed and I shall return from Wimbledon Park on next Thursday. It is a cross road from thence to Ockham so that I must return to town which also will be more convenient for my calculating people who will want direction. If you should be disengaged I will come down to you by coach on Saturday or Monday or any other day that week which you will fix. I hope this may not be too late to meet Lady Byron to whom I fear I have appeared very negligent.

It is an odd fatality but I seem always to neglect most those friends I most highly value. You have I think half found this out. It is certainly no small sacrifice I make for the sake of the calculating [machine] that I often forego the enjoyment of the society I most delight in.

With best regards to Lord Lovelace,

Believe me, Ever sincerely yours,

C. Babbage

Saturday would suit them perfectly, she said, but they hoped he would stay as far into the following week as possible. Surely the machine allowed him a holiday sometimes. Lady Noel Byron *would* be there.

The beginning and date of the next letter are missing, but it was written towards the end of 1839 after the birth of her third child and second son, Ralph Gordon Noel King, later thirteenth Baron Wentworth and second Earl of Lovelace.

She had quite made up her mind to have some instruction in town, said Lady Lovelace, but the difficulty was to find the man. She had a peculiar way of learning, and thought it must be a peculiar man to teach her successfully. She begged him not to consider her conceited, for she was sure she was the very last person to think over highly of herself; but she believed that she had the power of going just as far as she liked in such pursuits, and when there was so very decided a taste, she should almost say a *passion*, as she had for them, she questioned if there were not always some portion of natural genius even; at any rate, the taste was such that it must be gratified. She mentioned all this because she thought he was or might be in the way of meeting with the right sort of person, and she was sure he had at any rate the will to give her any assistance in his power.

To this he replied on 29th November 1839:

'I make a most ungrateful return for your kind letter from [illeg.]. I have lately been even more than usually occupied by the engine.

'I allowed myself ten days in Cheshire and finding this did not do I was obliged to go to Brighton for five days which restored me to the calculating state and I have been working very hard ever since.

'I have just arrived at an improvement which will throw back all my drawings full six months unless I succeed in carrying out some new views which may shorten the labour.

'I have now commenced the description of the engine so that I am fully occupied.

'I think your taste for mathematics is so decided that it ought not to be checked. I have been making enquiry but cannot find at present anyone at all to recommend to assist you. I will however not forget the search.

'The London world is very quiet at present. Mrs. De Morgan has just added a new philosopher to its population and Mr. Sheridan Knowles has written a most popular play called *Love* to which I have been a frequent attendant. I met the author yesterday at dinner at Mr. Rogers'.

'I could not by [any] possibility have visited you this year in the West, but I cherish the hope of getting a few days at Ockham when I can indulge in a little more recreation.

'Pray forgive my epistolary negligence.'

She returned to the subject of a tutor on 14th March 1840, for Charles Babbage had not succeeded in finding 'the right sort of person'. Should there seem no chance of the *great unknown* being found for her, she said, she had some idea of having instead for this season some German lessons. She knew a little already and intended to know more. Indirectly, she thought, it would bear on some of her objects.

On the back of this letter, possibly as a reminder to himself, he scribbled a reference to 'Our Great Unknown'.

The charm which he could exercise when in the mood and when with congenial companions can be inferred from her remarks written at Ockham, on 5th January 1841, by which time she was beginning to show specific interest in the analytical engine:

'You have put me into a dilemma, because I should naturally say—come on Friday, and come *again* rather later.

'If you come this week, you will I *believe* find us quite alone; if later, suppose about the 15th, there will probably be company. Now we like so much to have you in *either* circumstances; when alone, the pleasure of monopolizing you is so great; when in company, you make the company so *tenfold* agreeable, that *I* cannot choose between them. I can only say that we wish to see you at *all* times, and as much as possible.

'So I am afraid I have left you much where you were, and not helped you greatly to a decision.

'I much wish to have you here, and talk with you of some of my own doings, etc. Today I have been working much at *mathematics*; it has been bad for *out-doors*, and therefore I have got a lift at *in-door* pursuits.

'I must show you a certain book called my mathematical scrap-book.

'But pray do not think of coming for so *very short* a time as only 3 nights. It would be shameful!

'Some day or other you will have to put me in possession

of the main points relating to your engine. I have more reasons than one for desiring this.'

A week later, on 12th January, she was referring more explicitly to what she hoped to do for him, in return, perhaps, for having himself taken the place of the 'Great Unknown'.

'If you will come by the Railway on Friday, we will send a carriage to meet you at Weybridge, for the train that leaves Town about 4 o'clock and arrives at Weybridge about 5 o'clock.

'Bring warm coats or cloaks, as the carriage will be probably an open one. If you are a *skater*, pray bring skates to Ockham, that being the fashionable occupation here now, and one *I* have much taken to.

'I am very anxious to talk to you. I will give you a hint on *what*. It strikes me that at some future time (it might be even within 3 or 4 years, or it might be *many* years hence), *my head* may be made by you subservient to some of *your* purposes and plans. If so, *if* ever I could be worthy or capable of being *used* by you, my head will be yours; and it is on this that I wish to speak most seriously to you.

'You have always been a kind and real and most invaluable friend to *me*; and I would that I could in any way repay it, tho' I scarcely dare so exalt myself as to hope, however humbly, that I can ever be intellectually worthy to attempt serving *you*.'

The following month, on 22nd February 1841, she was writing again from Ockham Park, full of enthusiasm for her plans and the assistance she intended to give him. She believed she would perhaps pass Sunday evening with Mr. and Mrs. De Morgan, but, if not, would Charles come and spend it in St. James's Square? 'You see I am determined to celebrate the Sabbath *mathematically*, in one way or other.'

She had been at work very strenuously since she last saw him, and quite as successfully as before.

She was now studying attentively the finite differences and in this she had more particular interest, because she knew it bore directly on some of his business.

'Altogether I am going on well, and fast, as we might have anticipated; I think I am more determined than ever in my future plans; and I have quite made up my mind that nothing must be suffered to interfere with them. I intend to make such arrangements in Town as will secure me a couple of hours daily (with very few exceptions) for my studies. I think much of the possible (I believe I may say the *probable*) future connection between us; and it is an anticipation I increasingly like to dwell on. I think great good may be the results to *both* of us, and I suspect that the idea (which by the by is one that I believe I have long entertained in a vague and crude form), was one of those happy instincts which do occur to one sometimes so unaccountably and fortunately. At least, in my opinion; the results may ultimately prove it such.'

For most of the rest of that year Lady Lovelace was writing short notes on social topics. With some of her friends she sponsored a Welsh boy named Thomas, who played the Welsh harp with great talent. A concert was organized on 12th May, and enough money was raised to procure for him a year's professional training. On 6th April she left on the Boulogne boat for France, telling Charles that if he wished to write to her *poste restante*, Paris, would do as her address. Later, from St. James's Square she announced that she was taking stalls for the Italian opera, and was taking Miss King and Dr. King (her former tutor) and would he make a fourth?

It was on this or some similar occasion that Charles, bored by the opera, went behind the scenes to investigate the mechanism, and after much climbing and roaming about found himself in a dark abyss. Above his head a flat wooden roof was supported by upright timbers, 'some having intermediate stages like large dissecting tables'.

A bell rang, and a friendly scene-shifter hurried away, shouting out some instructions which Charles misunderstood, for he found himself on a platform six feet above the floor. Suddenly there was a flash of lightning, and looking up he was dazzled by the glare. Then 'two devils with long forked tails jumped upon the platform, one at each end'. They must have been more surprised to see him than he was to see them. As they approached the open trapdoor of the stage above, Devil

No. 1 confirmed, in answer to his enquiry, that a beam some feet higher would bear his weight. Charles leaped on to it and was congratulated by his friends, including, no doubt, Lady Lovelace, on his 'undeserved escape'.

A year elapsed before the next short note was written and it is of special interest for two reasons: it was the first in the series in which she addressed him as 'My dear Babbage', equivalent nowadays to the use of his Christian name, and, secondly, his own note which speaks for itself.

11 Aug. 1842

My dear Babbage,

Will you come on Saturday the 20th to visit us for 3 or 4 days? We expect Fonblanque and others . . . In haste.

Yours most sincerely,

A. Ada Lovelace

On the back Charles Babbage scribbled: 'I will endeavour to join you at Ockham on Sat. the 20th, but the state of drawings and a possible discussion with Sir R. Peel may prevent or deprive me of that pleasure.'

19

Fairy For Ever

*

MEANWHILE, in contrast to Charles's relations with Lady Lovelace at this time, those with his sons were not particularly happy, largely, it would seem, because none of them was anything like his intellectual equal. Even the otherwise reliable Herschel had disappointed him by marrying a girl named Laura Jones, whom they had met at Clifton in 1836. 'The marriage', said Henry, 'did not please our father.'

He seems to have been little better pleased with Dugald and Henry, both of whom on leaving University College School went to University College for two years, when they were promoted to frock-coats and a dress allowance of £18 a year, receiving some weekly pocket money from their grandmother, with whom they continued to live at 5 Devonshire Street.

They spent some of their time in the workshop and drawing office at 1 Dorset Street, learning from a workman named Garton various jobs such as turning, filing and fitting; from Jarvis and Creedy in the drawing office they acquired a little draughtsmanship. Jarvis, who earned 2s. 6d. an hour, 'made all the beautiful drawings for the analytical engine'. Creedy, a mathematician and a keen analyst, 'was unfortunately very irregular in his habits'.

In 1840 Herschel, who had been pupil and then assistant to Mark Isambard Brunel on the Great Western Railway, was taken by Brunel to Italy to make surveys for the projected Genoa–Turin railway. Dugald followed as pupil to Herschel in the spring of 1840 and left Dorset Street in a vehicle belonging to Herschel. 'A light thing, very fit for a park, but utterly unfit for a travelling carriage', said Henry. Into this were packed Herschel's wife, her baby and sister, Dugald and a maid-servant occupying the back seat. Henry well remembered his father's 'evident contempt for their arrangements, or rather want of arrangement'. Charles was probably comparing the equipage with his own calash, built at Vienna twelve years before.

In the autumn of 1842, having unsuccessfully formed various plans for Henry, he asked his son what he wished to do. Henry replied that he would like to go to India in the military service of the East India Company, and that he would study the languages and qualify for an appointment open to military officers. Charles made no comment, but mentioned the matter to his friends, as a result of which a cadetship was offered for Henry.

The boy spent the last few weeks of his stay in England at 1 Dorset Street, but saw little of his father, who went much into society at this time, and in February 1843 'had no less than 13 invitations for every day of the month, Sundays included, to dinners and parties of one sort or another'. He sacrificed however some of them to be with Henry. And among the few pieces of advice which he gave to his son was this—extra-ordinarily enough, it would seem, from Charles Babbage—'Never to *fancy* anyone offended with me if he seemed not as pleased as usual to see me, the difference might be caused by ill health, or plenty of other reasons unconnected with me'.

Mrs. Benjamin Babbage, now an old lady, was much upset by the parting from her grandson. But Charles said farewell in his library at 1 Dorset Street and did not see Henry into the cab. The boy had to wait at Portsmouth for his ship, and while there an elderly gentleman came in with his son, asking Henry and other passengers to keep an eye on him. 'I could not help contrasting his tender anxiety for his son with that of my own father.'

All Charles's tender anxiety seems at this time to have been focused on Lady Lovelace, for he was undoubtedly astonished by the rapid progress she was making in her studies. In the last year or two she had not only mastered the details of the analytical engine but also those of symbolic logic, of which Thomas Hobbes of Malmesbury was an early exponent.

If the views of Hobbes were tenable, that we represented in our reasoning operations the sum total from addition of parcels, or a remainder by subtraction of one from another, it seemed to follow that we could accurately express those operations in the same way as in algebra, so that the collection of parcels into a whole would be aptly indicated by the sign $+$, while the inverse operation would be properly represented by the sign $-$.

By the end of June 1843 Lady Lovelace had made such progress that she had translated Menabrea's paper and was already annotating it. On 30th June Charles Babbage, having said farewell to Henry, wrote to her about one of the most difficult of the notes, in which she explained in abstruse mathematical terms the variables for data, working variables and variables for results.

'I am delighted with Note D. It is in your usual clear style and requires only one trifling alteration which I will make. This arises from the circumstances of our not having yet had time to examine the outline of the mechanical part.

'Only three kinds of variable cards are used.

'1st. Those which give off a variable from the store to the mill and leave zeros on the variable itself.

'2nd. Those which give off a variable from the store to the mill and at the same time (or in the same turn of the hand) retain the same variable in the inner [?] place.

'3rd. Those which order any variable in which only zeros exist to receive a result from the mill. I propose to omit one paragraph which I have marked in pencil and the rest is quite correct, as however I suppose you will wish to see the change I return you the sheet. I have not yet received a proof and shall enquire about it tomorrow.

'I enclose a copy of the integration. I am still working at some most entangled notations of division but see my way through them at the expense of heavy labour, from which I shall not shrink as long as my head can bear it. I have been somewhat impeded however for the last few days. Your latest information was the most agreeable.'

There was an abrupt change in the tone of her reply. She was no longer the diffident, hero-worshipping beginner. Conscious of her growing power, she was becoming more and more self-confident. In all her subsequent letters about her work she was arrogant, autocratic, dictatorial, high-handed, flirtatious, girlish, boyish, childish and affectionate in turn; and, when she spoke of her ill health, very touching. Like Charles himself she was fully aware of her own genius, although she may have used the term in its contemporary meaning—great talent or gift. And she was very much the daughter of Byron in her determination not to have her sentences altered. Charles took these strictures (and what might have seemed rudeness to a man so much older than herself) in good part, because no doubt she *was* the daughter of Byron, but also because he was an old friend of the family, because she was a young woman and, perhaps of greater importance than anything else, because she was, unlike his own sons, his intellectual equal. She wrote:

'I am much annoyed at your having altered my Note. You know I am always willing to make *any* required alterations myself, but that I cannot endure another person to meddle with my sentences. If I disapprove, therefore, I hope I may be able to alter in the *revise*, supposing you have sent away the proof and notes. Then I cannot agree to your not having effaced the *paragraph*. In *one* instance, at any rate, if not in all, it is very necessary that the paragraph *should* be effaced; as it makes a division in the sense where there should be a perfect continuity.

'In short I am somewhat disturbed about the matter altogether. I meant to make a slight alteration too in one of the smaller notes which I sent, the one relating to the substituting zero for a number that has been packed off to the mill. *Half after two* on Monday will suit me better than *three o'clock*.

'I suppose that next week will conclude *all* the corrections and revisions. I hope so.

'And I must then beg you to deliver to me, *tant soit plus note*, all the documents I am at present to have in order to commence work upon.

'I think much about the other scientific matters and find that my plans and ideas keep gaining in clearness, and assuming more and more of the *crystalline*, and less and less of the nebulous form.'

On Sunday morning, 2nd July 1843, she wrote to say that she was reflecting much on the work and duties for Charles and the engine, which were to occupy her, she supposed, during the next two or three years. She had some excellent ideas on the subject, and intended to incorporate into one department of her labours a complete reduction to a system of the principles and methods of discovery; elucidating the same with examples. She was already noting down a list of discoveries hitherto made, in order to examine their history, origin and progress. One first and main point, whenever and wherever she introduced the subject, would be first to define and to classify all that was to be legitimately included under the term *discovery*. 'There will be a fine field for my *clear*, logical and accurate mind, to work its powers upon; and to develope its *metaphysical* genius, which is not the least amongst its qualifications and characteristics.'

On the same day Charles replied to her previous letter and called attention to two mistakes of her own.

'If you are as fastidious about the acts of your friends as you are about those of your pen, I much fear I shall equally lose your friendship and your notes. I like much the improved form of the Bernouilli note but can judge of it better when I have the diagram and notation.

'I am very reluctant to return the admirable and philosophic view of the Anal. Engine contained in Note A. Pray do not alter it and do let me have it returned on Monday. I send also the rest of Note D. There is still one trifling misapprehension about the variable cards. A variable card may order any number of variables to receive the *same number* upon them at the *same* instant of time. But a variable card never can be directed to order more than *one* variable to be given off at once because the mill could not receive it and the mechanism would not permit it. All this it was impossible for you to know by intuition and the more I read your notes the more surprised I am at them and regret not having earlier explored so rich a vein of the noblest metal.

'The account of them stands thus:

A sent to Lady L.	E With C.B.
B with C.B.	F Retained by Lady L.
C Ditto	G Where is it gone?
D Sent to Lady L.	H With C.B.'

The confusion over Note G or H was to continue to the end of the revision and proof correcting, but in the final version G was substituted for H.

She wrote the same evening:

'I have worked most successfully all day. You will admire the *table and diagram* extremely. They have been made out with extreme care and all the *indices* most minutely and scrupulously attended to. Lord L. is at this moment kindly *inking it all over for me*. I had to do it pencil. You must bring *all* the notes with you tomorrow as I have observations to make on each one, and especially on this final one *H*. I have never [illeg.] a note G. I do not know why I chose H instead of G and thus insulted the other worthy letter. I cannot imagine what you mean about the variable cards; since I never either supposed in my own mind that one variable card *could give* off more than one variable at a time, nor have I (as far as I can make out) expressed such an idea in any passage whatever.

'I cannot find what I fancied I had put in Note A; so I return it whole and sound, for your speedy relief. I send back Note D. You will find the only alteration I wished to make pinned over in the upper part of sheet 2.

'So I now retain nothing but the Note F, which I shall give you tomorrow.

'Lord L. has put up, I find, in a separate cover, all that belongs to Note H. (He is quite enchanted with the *beauty* and *symmetry* of the table and diagram.) No—I find I can put in Note D with H.'

After dealing with a question of pure mathematics in her next letter, dated 4th July 1843, Lady Lovelace mentioned a subject that was greatly exercising her mind. Lord Lovelace had suggested her signing the translation and notes, by which, she said, he meant simply putting at the end of the former: 'translated by A.A.L.' and adding to each note the initials A.A.L. It was not her wish to proclaim who had written it; at the same time she rather wished to uphold anything that might tend thereafter to individualize and identify it with other productions of the said A.A.L. The problem was a knotty one, for it was considered unfeminine at that time for any woman, and least of all a peeress, to sign any literary production.

Thirdly, she had analysed the question of the numbers of variable cards, as mentioned in the final Note H (or G) and found that between them Charles and she had made a mess of it, for which, she added, she could perfectly account, in a very natural manner.

She enclosed what she wished to insert instead of that which was now there. She thought the present wrong passage was only about eight or ten lines, and was she believed on the second of the three great sheets that were to follow the diagram.

'The fact is that if my own exposition about the variable cards in Note D had been strictly followed by myself, in Note H, this would not have occurred. The confusion has arisen simply from the circumstances of applying to the variable cards, facts which relate to the *operation* cards.'

In Note D it was very well and lucidly demonstrated that every single operation demanded the use of at least three variable cards. It did not signify whether the operations were in cycles or not, a million successive additions $+ + +$ would each demand the use of three variable cards, under ordinary circumstances, for Note H, the erroneous lines were founded on the hasty supposition that the cycle or necessary group, of operation cards (13 . . . 23), would be fed by a cycle or recurring group of variable cards.

She enclosed what she believed it ought to be. If already gone to the printer, the passage could be altered in the proofs, unless Charles could call at the printers and there paste over the amendments.

She then, as she was so often to do, referred to her ill health.

'I can scarcely describe to you how *very* ill and harassed I

felt yesterday. Pray excuse any abruptness or other unpleasant-
ness of manner, if there were any. I am breathing *well* again
today, and am much better in all respects; owing to Dr. L's
remedies, he certainly does seem to understand the case, I
mean the treatment of it, which is the main thing. As for the
theory of it, he says truly that *time* and *providence* alone can
develope that. It is so *anomalous* an affair altogether. I think
of my having to *walk* (or rather *run*) to the station in half an
hour last evening; while I suppose *you* were feasting and flirting
in luxury and ease at your dinner. It must be a very pleasant
and merry sort of thing to have a *fairy* in one's service (minus
limbs?). I envy you.

'*I*, poor little fairy, can only get dull heavy *mortals* to wait on
me!'

In her next two letters she again referred to the variable
cards, and then, from the succeeding passages, one gains an
exceedingly interesting insight into her character, and the way
in which her mind was working.

'Why does my friend prefer imaginary roots for our friendship? Just because she happens to have some of that imagination which *you* would deny her to possess; and therefore
she enjoys a little *play* and *scope* for it now and then. Besides
this, I deny the *fairyism* to be certainly imaginary (& it is to
the fairy similies that I suppose you allude). That brain of
mine is something more than merely mortal, as time will
show. (If only my breathing and some other etceteras do not
make too rapid a progress *towards* instead of *from* mortality.)

'Before ten years are over, the Devil's in it if I haven't
sucked out some of the life blood from the mysteries of *this*
universe, & in a way that no purely mortal lips or brains
could do. No one knows what almost *awful* energy and power
lie yet undeveloped in that *wiry* little system of mine. I say
awful, because you may imagine what it might be under
certain circumstances. Lord L. sometimes says "What a
General you would make!" Fancy me in times of social and
political trouble (had wordly power, rule & ambition been
my line, which it now never could be.) . . .

'It is well for the world that my line & ambition is ever the *spiritual*, and that I have not taken it into my head to deal with the sword, poison and intrigue, in the place of x, y & z . . .

'Yours, *Fairy* for ever,

A.A.L.'

On 6th July she sent the corrected 'first sheet' to Charles, having taken great pains with it, and thought it much improved. Like all who have had to see matter through the press, she was to complain bitterly about the printer, now and later on. On this occasion he had made one or two paragraphs where none should have existed, and had also failed to print some words in italics that ought to have been so expressed.

She believed that the notes would be far easier to correct than the translation, because she had taken so much more trouble with them. She hoped so, 'for it is damnably troublesome work and plagues me'. In a postscript she added that she meant to put her initials to all the notes, but to leave the translation without.

20

'An Uncommonly Fine Baby'

*

CHARLES BABBAGE in the meantime seems to have been thinking of drawing Prince Albert's attention to Lady Lovelace's work, the idea probably having been suggested by an event of the previous year, when Count Mensdorf, the Queen's uncle, visited London, and the Duke of Wellington took him, with the Prince, to Dorset Street to see the difference engine. Although Charles was afterwards to suspect the Prince of being one of those concerned in excluding the difference engine from the 1851 Exhibition, he was delighted with him on this occasion.

In the drawing-room he showed the distinguished visitors the portrait of Jacquard which had been given to him. It was a sheet of woven silk, framed and glazed, and looking so exactly like an engraving that two Royal Academicians had been deceived.

'Oh,' remarked the Duke, when Charles drew attention to it, 'that engraving?'

'No,' said Prince Albert, 'it is not an engraving.'

For this extremely well-informed remark Charles thought him 'a good man and true'. But when he mentioned his scheme to Lady Lovelace she said: 'I have been considering about Prince Albert, but I much doubt the expediency of it; however there is time enough to consider of this.' Her will seems to have prevailed. There appears to be no record of a copy of the translation and notes being sent to the Prince.

On 10th July 1843 she wrote to Charles Babbage: 'I am working very hard for you; like the Devil in fact; (which perhaps I *am*.)

Portion of Babbage's difference engine.
Crown copyright, Science Museum, London

Portion of Babbage's
analytical engine,
front view.
*Crown copyright,
Science Museum, London*

Portion of Babbage's
analytical engine,
with additions, 1910.
*Crown copyright,
Science Museum, London*

'I *think* you will be pleased. I have made [what] appear to me some very important extensions and improvements. Why I now write is to beg you will send down to the [St. James's] Square before tomorrow evening Brooke's *Formulae* and also the *Reports of the Royal Society* on your machine.

'I suppose you can get it easily, and I particularly want to see it, *before* I see *you* on Wed. morning.

'It appears to me that I am working up the notes with much success; and that even if the book be delayed in its publication a week or two, in consequence, it would be worth Mr. Taylor's while to wait. I *will* have it *well* and *fully* done; or not at all.

'I want to put in something about Bernouilli's numbers, in one of my notes, as an example of how an implicit function may be worked out by the engine, without having been worked out by human head and hands first. Give me the necessary data and formulae.'

She was still getting on with the corrections on 11th July and hoping that he would attend carefully to her criticisms about the preface. Two days later she asked him to join her at St. James's Square at 9 a.m. She named so early an hour because she thought they would have much to do. She had been very unwell again, partly with distressing indigestion and partly with the miserable and changed weather; partly, too, she might perhaps have added, with the exhausting labour of working so hard against time. She then remarked that she wished to know something more about how he managed the imaginary quantities.

Charles found himself again in trouble on 19th July 1843.

It was quite evident, she declared, that he had been looking over the superseded sheet 4, instead of the corrected one. All his remarks seemed to apply to the former; and the latter was passed without notice. 'Pray be with me at *half past nine o'clock* tomorrow morning if you can, as I am exceedingly disturbed about it. Lord L. is so vexed too at everything not being done, that I am half beside myself.'

And he was pressing her in several ways at the moment, most unfortunately, and among it all, she really would be a long time, and would lose her head for everything. She begged

Charles to look carefully over the *real* papers. She sent them together (and the superseded one she had put separately). She really could not believe it to be incorrect, for nothing could exceed the care with which she had gone over it. 'But the fact is I am plagued out of my life just now.'

She added that she had made out a list of the operations which calculated each coefficient for each variable, and had attached it to Charles's own memorandum.

She was still in difficulties a day or two later.

My dear Babbage,

I am in much dismay at having got into so amazing a quagmire and botheration with these *numbers*, that I cannot possibly get the thing done today. I have no doubt it will all come out clear enough tomorrow; & I shall send you a parcel up, as early in the day as I can. So do not be uneasy, (tho' at this moment I am in a charming state of confusion; but it is that sort of confusion which is of a very *bubble* nature).

I am now going out on horse back, *tant mieux*.

Yours,

Puzzle-pate

She asked him on 25th July 1843 whether he could be with her in Town at 4 p.m. the following Thursday, as she could not feel happy about all the notes without reading them over aloud to him before they were finally printed. Could he also give her Thursday evening for the opera? Again she changed her mind: 'I shall not put my initials to my notes, but I wish them to be translator's notes.'

On the following days she said that after working almost incessantly since seven o'clock in the morning, until forced to give in from sheer inability to concentrate any longer, she found only one sheet completed, but she would send a servant up in the morning by the ten o'clock train with the rest. 'You cannot conceive the trouble I have had with the trigonometrical Note E. In fact no one but me, I really believe, would have doggedly stuck to it, as I have been doing, in all its wearing minutiæ.'

She was very uneasy because she had not heard from Charles, and feared 'some disaster or other'. She hoped that all of Note G was forthcoming and that he had received all her communications safely. She thought that he had better do the second revise of the translation for her. If he would compare it carefully with her first revise it would hardly be necessary, she thought, for her to go over it again. 'I suppose I ought to take it for granted that *no news* is *good news*, but I am in a sad fidget.'

She added that she had sent him 'since Saturday' the whole of the revised translation and the corrected proofs of Notes A, B and C. And she now sent parts of D and E. She would send the remainder of these two and all of Note F. The very little bit she had of Note G she would retain until she got the remainder. She hoped that the printer was getting on with what had been sent back. She wrote the same evening:

'I send you what I have of Note E, which is not *nearly* all. So you must not judge of it, as it is. I am becoming sadly *over* worked, & have scarcely brains left for anything.

'I wonder how you will like my further *addition* to the upper indices. I half fear *not*. But I can cancel it, if you disapprove.

'No more to-night, for I can neither talk, write, nor think common sense. And yet I feel more like a *fairy* than ever (but I suppose *that* idea is *uncommon* and not *common* sense.)

'Yours,
Addlepate'

A letter from Charles had evidently crossed hers, in which he had complimented her on the notes, for the next day she was greatly uplifted and excited.

'I am happy to find that the *Notes* will require very little correction indeed.

'To say the truth, I *am* rather *amazed* at them and cannot help being struck quite *malgre moi* with the really masterly nature of the style and its superiority to that of the memoir itself.

'I have made Lord L. laugh much by the dryness with which I remarked, "Well, I am very much satisfied with this first child of mine. He is an uncommonly fine baby, and will grow to be a *man* of the first magnitude and power."

'I approve your alteration in the preface, excepting that I think the word "so" comes in both awkwardly and super-fluously. Pray efface it, and let it stand "*of the money to be ex-pended*". That little word spoils it.

'You will be amused and somewhat triumphant, perhaps, when I own that I entirely approve your alteration to my foot-note . . . & only find the insertion of one single word (& that not in the part you meddled with) to be a [desideratum?]

'Altogether I think things are doing very well. I expect to have all the notes done by Monday, & the subsequent revise of them will probably be but a very trifling matter.

'Lord L. seems pleased beyond measure with the very *learned* and knowing aspect of my baby's physiognomy which he has glanced at.'

A day later she was at St. James's Square and another dispute arose over Charles's carelessness, or, rather, forget-fulness, due to long years of intense, abstract thought.

'The beginning of Note G (by which I mean the Table and all that *precedes* it) never has been returned into my hands; a small part of the remainder *was*, but *that* I speedily gave you back, and there it is, now printed. The missing part *must* be either at your house or at the printers; & it seems to me very unlikely that *you* should have retained it. So altogether I would wager almost anything that it is at the *office*; or that if lost it has been lost there.

'At the same time, I have always fancied that you were a little harum-scarum & inaccurate now & then about the exact *order & arrangements* of sheets, pages, & paragraphs etc. (Witness that paragraph which you so carelessly *pasted over*!) I *suppose* that I must set to work to write something *better* if I can, as a substitute. The *same precisely* I could not recall. I think I should be able in a couple of days to do something. However I should be deucedly inclined to *swear* at you, I will allow.

'I desire my messenger to wait; as it is possible you may have something to communicate more agreeable.'

Back at Ockham Park on 29th July 1843, she said that she had been hard at work all day intending to send him the diagram and all, quite complete; and then to her horror had found that the table and diagram (over which she had been spending infinite patience and pains) were seriously wrong in one or two points. She had done them, however, in a beautiful manner, much improved upon their *first* edition of a table and diagram, but unluckily she had made some errors.

She sent all the final Note H, excepting the said table and diagram, and returned Note C in which ('for a wonder') she could find nothing to alter or mend. Note F she still retained, since she found that she had (as she suspected) put into it one or two things that were inconsistent with what she had subsequently written. The sheet of Note D she returned, having pinned over the effaced part the alteration she wished to make instead of omitting the passage altogether.

She begged him to send by her servant (who would call in the morning for his orders) the other sheets of Note D, as she wished to alter one or two passages in consequence of his information of the morning. She also begged for Note A in which she remembered a wrong passage about variable cards.

'Now *pray* attend strictly to my requests, or you will cause me very serious annoyance. I shall be up betimes to-morrow morning, & finish off the table & diagram, so as to send it to you by post; to-gether with the amendments in what my servant shall bring me down to-morrow morning from you.' He would therefore have a budget on Monday morning, and she intended to go to Town herself that day for a few hours, in order to run over a few things with him finally. Would he be so kind as to be in the Square at two o'clock? 'I fear you will think me *detestably persevering*.'

It was now the printer's turn to come under fire. She reported (on 30th July 1843) that she was vexed beyond measure to find that instead of inserting her *corrected* table in the revise (for the example A + bsc' A + B cos' sc) the printer had left it exactly as it was before. 'Pray see about it immediately; it is exceedingly careless and annoying.' Out of several corrections made, not one was inserted, she complained, neither were the upper indices added, nor the little footnote. She returned all the latter part of the revise, and the corresponding proofs, that Charles might look to the matter forthwith. 'I cannot account for such negligence.' In all the tables, but especially that for some of the equations, the Vs were unfortunately small in proportion to the indices, which made the letters far less distinct to the eye than they should be.

Charles now became the target. She found herself in some distress for the original memoir, which he should have sent back. 'I do not think you possess half my forethought, & powers of foreseeing all *possible* contingencies (probable & *improbable*, just alike).'

She was glad to see the sheets she returned, so clean on the whole. She expected to send up the rest of the revise on the following day, and Note A by her governess in the middle of the day, and more by post. She would work most diligently, but wished to revise the notes herself. Perhaps he would send someone to Ockham the moment he got them; she would attend immediately and send them back by the same or some other special messenger.

She had begun his *Examples of the Calculus of Functions*, appended to Herschel's *Examples of Finite Differences*. This would familiarize her a little with the subject; but it was necessary to obtain various other papers, referred to by Charles at the end of the examples.

'How *very* careless of you to forget that Note, and how much waiting on & service you owe me, to compensate!' she concluded. 'I am in good spirits, for I hope another year will *really* make me something of an *Analyst*. The more I study the more irresistible do I feel my genius for it to be. I do *not* believe that my father was (or ever could have been) such a poet as I shall be an *Analyst* & Metaphysician, for with me the two go together indissolubly.'

By the 1st August she had again worked herself into a state of excitement and nervous tension.

'I am half beside myself with hurry and work. I could not get anything done in time to send by coach this morning, and now I am obliged still to retain *one* sheet; which however I hope to send you by an occasion to-morrow afternoon.

'Note B has plagued me to death, altho' I have made but little alteration in it. Such alterations as there *are*, however, happen to have been very tiresome and to have demanded minute consideration & many nice adjustments. It is a very excellent Note. I wish you were as accurate, & as much to be relied on as I am myself.

'You might often save me much trouble, if you were, whereas you in reality *add* to my trouble not infrequently, and there is at any rate always the anxiety of *doubting* if you will not get me into a scrape, even when you don't.

'By the way, I hope you do not take upon yourself to alter any of my corrections. I *must* beg you not. They all have some very sufficient reason, and you have made a pretty mess & confusion in one or two places (which I will show you sometime) where you have ventured in my M.S.S. to insert or alter a phrase or word, & have utterly muddled the sense.

'I could not conceive at first in one or two places what had happened to my sentences, tho' I soon saw they were *patchwork*, & not my own, & found it so on referring to the MS.

'I fear you will think this a very *cross* letter. Never mind. I am a good little thing, after all.

'Later P.S. It is impossible to send you anything but Note B and C; (& this partly owing to some wrong references & blunderations of your own.) Do not be afraid, for I will work like the devil early to-morrow morning.'

Six days later Charles sent her the revise and its alterations, asking her to return it by post to Mr. Taylor's printing office, Red Lion Court, Fleet Street. The final revise of the translation he hoped to send to the printer that night, so that they could start putting it into pages. He had suggested two amendments. He sent in another cover the last of the notes and the 'great notation'.

On 8th August he asked her to send some further proofs direct to the printer, as there was little time to spare. 'The Number *ought* to be out in the course of a very few days', he said.

21

'My Dear and Much Admired Interpretress'

*

A FTER all this feverish activity, this indescribable intellectual labour and confusion, this frenzied posting of servants
backwards and forwards between the country and London,
the translation and notes came out towards the end of August
1843.

Only those who have been misunderstood, misrepresented
and traduced by their countrymen will understand Charles
Babbage's feelings towards his interpretress, and only those who
have experienced the difficulty of obtaining correct translations
of scientific data can appreciate the skill with which Lady
Lovelace rendered Menabrea's paper into English.

'General Menabrea himself was very much surprised to find
his memoir not only accurately translated, but with interesting
scientific commentaries added to it, by an unknown author
whose initials he could not connect with any of the mathematicians of the day. After diligent enquiries he was informed that
the author was Lady Lovelace, Lord Byron's only daughter.'

The writer of these words was the Prince de Polignac, son
of the Minister of Charles X of France, who, in 1911, when he
was an old man of eighty, sought confirmation from Lady Anne
Blunt that the unknown author was her mother. Lady Anne
confirmed it, and the Prince wrote to her from the Hotel
Meurice in Paris, thanking her for the assistance she had given
him in a matter of scientific interest. He added:

'Be assured that I have a keen appreciation of the filial
sentiments so handsomely expressed in your letter, and trust
that your kind instrumentality will help to revive before the

scientific world the merits of your departed mother, and shed a new lustre on her memory.'

Another forty years were to elapse before these merits were to be fully revived, or, to quote Lady Lovelace herself, 'the uncommonly fine baby' grew to be 'a man of the first magnitude and power'.

Menabrea began by stressing the dissimilarity between the difference engine and the analytical engine. All methods of trial and guesswork were excluded in the analytical engine, and only the direct processes admitted, he said. It was necessarily so, for the machine was not a thinking being but simply an automaton which acted according to the laws imposed upon it.

On this the translator commented: 'This must not be understood in too unqualified a manner. The engine is capable, under certain circumstances, of feeling about to discover which of two or more possible contingencies has occurred, and of then shaping its future course accordingly.'

Menabrea then described how the machine materially represented numbers. A pile or vertical column consisted of an indefinite number of circular discs, all pierced through their centres by a common axis, around which each of them could take an independent rotary movement. The arrangements could be divided into two classes, the first relating to the operations, the second to the variables, the latter meaning that which indicated the columns to be operated on. The operations themselves were executed by the mill. The mill was the part of the machine that worked, and the columns of variables were where the results were represented and arranged.

After describing the Jacquard loom, Menabrea remarked that the analytical engine contained two principal kinds of cards, operation cards and variable cards. He gave as an example the resolution of two equations of the first degree with two unknown quantities. Above every column, both of the mill and the store, was a disc, similar to the discs of which the columns consisted. According to whether the digit or disc was even or uneven, the number inscribed on the column below would be considered positive or negative. Some of the difficulties which the engine must surmount were examined.

'Certain functions necessarily change in nature when they pass through zero or infinity, or whose values cannot be admitted when they pass these limits', said Menabrea. 'When such cases present themselves, the machine is able, by means of a bell, to give notice that the passage through zero or infinity is taking place, and it then stops until the attendant has again set it in action for whatever process it may next be desired that it shall perform.'

The author then referred to a third species of cards, the cards of numbers. The numbers of Bernouilli and others frequently occurred in calculations. To avoid computing them every time certain cards could be combined specially in order to give them ready made into the mill.

There was no limit to the number of cards that could be used. Certain materials woven by the Jacquard loom required not less than 20,000.

The whole intellectual labour would be limited to the preparation of the formula.[1] The advantages were rigid accuracy and printing, economy of time, and economy of intelligence, sparing intellectual labour for more profitable employment.

It was by the laborious route of analysis that the man of genius must reach truth, Menabrea concluded. But he could not pursue this unless guided by numbers, for without them it was impossible to raise the veil which enveloped the mysteries of nature.

Then followed the translator's notes, each of which, in the end, she had initialled.[2]

Lady Lovelace ended her notes by 'following in detail the steps through which the engine could compute the Numbers of Bernouilli this being (in the form in which we shall deduce it) a rather complicated example of its powers'.

Just how complicated it was will be seen from the reproduction facing page 97.

Now that it was in print, the author was 'well satisfied on the whole' with her work, but, like most authors, felt that she could do it far better if she could start all over again.

1. Or, as we should say now, the programming.
2. See Appendix A, page 261.

Charles, however, still felt it was worth an original paper, and was too good for notes. He wrote on 5th August 1843:

'Today I saw Wheatstone and proposed to him a plan which will fulfil *all* your conditions and some of mine. He approves of it and thinks it will be adopted. If it is I shall write by Monday's post.'

In the meantime Lady Lovelace had misunderstood him, for he added on 8th August:

'I have nothing to add at present except that you did me injustice in supposing I wished you to break any engagement with the Editor. I wished you to ask him to allow you to withdraw from it. Had the Editor been in England I believe he would at my request have inserted my defence or foreborne to have printed the paper. As it stands I have done all I can at present to defend myself and having failed in the most important part shall make the best I can of the rest.'

She insisted that to go back on her word and withdraw the notes would have been dishonourable in the circumstances. He was annoyed about this and she went to very great lengths on 11th August to soothe his injured feelings, at the same time stressing some of his faults.

His note, she said, demanded a very full reply from her, the writer being 'so old and so esteemed a friend, and one whose genius I not only so *highly appreciate myself* but *wish to see fairly appreciated by others*'. Were it not for this desire, which Lord Lovelace and herself had more warmly at heart than he was as yet at all aware of, coupled with their long established regard and friendship, she would say that the less notice she took of his note the better, and that it was only worthy to be thrown aside with a smile of contempt. It was impossible to misunderstand the tone of it and she would not pretend to do so. And, as she knew he would not be explicit enough to describe the real state of his feelings towards her at this time, she would do it for him.

'You feel, my dear Babbage, that *I* have (tho' in a negative manner) *added* to the list of injuries & of disappointments & of mis-comprehensions that you have already experienced in a life by no means smooth or fortunate, you *know* this is your feeling; & that you are deeply hurt about it; & you endeavour to derive a poor & sorry consolation from such sentiments as "Well, she doesn't *know* or *intend* the injury & mischief she has done." '

After further remarks of this kind she said that her engagement was unconditional and that she had no right to withdraw the article on grounds subsequently thought of.

'But with the circumstances of your happening to be a private friend of my own & of my therefore being too happy & delighted to make my [illeg.] engagement especially pleasing & useful to you, they had nothing to do. Consequently, because my private friend wished it (however justly) this could form no real & equitable ground for withdrawing the article.'

She did not deny that his views might be higher, juster, wiser than her own. But her moral standard, such as it was, she must stick to, so long as it was her moral standard. And it would be useless trying to make him see through her glasses, for, besides the fact that they might be as far as his from reflecting quite truly, no one could alter the views of a lifetime.

But she did wish him to understand that she believed herself (however erroneous the belief might be) to have forwarded his interests far more by allowing the article to appear than she would have done by any of the courses he had suggested.

'I *have* a right to expect from you the belief that I do sincerely & honestly take this view. For if *your* knowledge of *me* does not furnish sufficient grounds for doing so, then I can only say that *no* mutual knowledge of any two human beings in this life can give stable & fixed grounds for faith & confidence. Then adieu to *all* trust, & to anything more generous in this world!'

She now came to a practical question respecting the future, and this, as will be seen later on, raises some interesting questions, for throughout the rest of her letter she gave no explicit account of what it was exactly she had in mind. Furthermore, from her reference to his love of fame and glory, and her own attitude in this respect, the inference may well be that the work she was asking him to do would have to be done in the utmost secrecy.

His affairs had been and were deeply occupying both herself and Lord Lovelace, she said. Their thoughts as well as their conversation had been upon them. And the result was that they had plans for him, which she did not think fit at present to communicate to him; but which she would either develop or else throw her energies, time and pen into some other department of truth and science, according to the reply she received from him. She besought him therefore deeply and seriously to ponder over the question how far he could subscribe to her conditions or not. She gave to him the first choice and offer of her services and her intellect. She hoped he would not lightly reject them. She said this entirely for his own sake. Her channels for developing and training her scientific and literary powers were various, and some of them very attractive. But she wished her old friend to have the *refusal*.

'Firstly: I want to know whether if I continue to work *on* or *about* your own great subject, you will undertake to abide wholly by the judgment of myself (or of any persons whom you may now please to name as referees,) whenever we may differ on all *practical* matters relating to whatever can involve relations with any fellow creature or fellow creatures.

'Secondly: Can you undertake to give your mind *wholly* & *undividedly*, as a primary object that no engagement is to interfere with, to the consideration of all these matters in which I shall at times require your intellectual assistance & supervision; & can you promise not to slur & hurry things over, or to mislay, & allow confusion & mistakes to enter into documents, etc.?

'Thirdly: if I am able to lay before you in the course of a year or two, explicit & honourable propositions for *consulting your engine* (such as are approved by persons whom you may *now* name to be referred to for their approbation) would there be any chance of you allowing myself & such parties to conduct the business for you; your own undivided energies being devoted to the execution of the work, and all other matters being arranged for you on terms which your *own* friends should approve?'

He would wonder over this last query, but she strongly

advised him not to reject it as whimsical. He did not know the grounds she had for believing that such a contingency might come within her power; and she wished to know before she allowed her mind to employ its energies any further on the subject that she would not be wasting thought and power for no purpose or result.

At the same time she felt she must place the whole of his relations with her in a fair and just light; their motives, and ways of meaning things, were very widely apart; and it might be an anxious question for him to decide how far the advantages and expediency of enlisting a mind of her particular class in his service could overbalance the disadvantages from her point of view. Her own uncompromising principle was to try to love truth and God before fame and glory or even just appreciation; and to believe generously and unwaveringly in the good of human nature (however dormant and latent it might often seem).

'*Yours* is to love truth & God (yes, deeply & constantly); but to love *fame* & *glory*, *honours*, *yet more*. You will deny this, but in all your intercourse with *every* human being (as far as I know & see of it) it is a *practically paramount* sentiment. Mind, I am not *blaming* it. I simply state my belief in the *fact*. One fact may be a very noble & beautiful fact. That is another question. Far be it from *me* to disclaim the influence of *ambition* & *fame*. No living soul ever was more imbued with it than myself; and my own view of duty is that it behoves me to place this great & useful quality in its *proper relations* and subordination; but I certainly would not deceive myself or others by pretending that it is other than a very important motive & ingredient to my character & nature.

'I wish to add my mite towards *expounding* & *interpreting* the Almighty, & His laws & works, for the most effective use of mankind, and certainly I should feel it no small glory if I were enabled to be one of His most noted prophets (using this word in my own peculiar sense) in this world. And I should undoubtedly prefer being *known* as a benefactor of this description, to being equally great in fact, but promulgating truths from obscurity and oblivion.'

At the same time she was not sure that thirty years hence she might put even so much value as this upon human fame. Every year added to the unlimited nature of her trust and hope in the Creator, and decreased her value for her relations with mankind. Through her present relations with man, she was doubtless to become fit for relations of another order hereafter; perhaps directly with the great Power Himself.

'My dear friend, if you knew what *sad* & *direful* experience I have had in ways of which you cannot be aware, you would feel that *some weight is* due to my feelings about God & man. As it is you will only smile & say "Poor little thing, she knows nothing of life or wickedness."

'Such as my principles are, & the conditions (founded on them) on which alone you may command my services, I have now stated them; to just such extent as I think is absolutely necessary for any comfortable understanding & co-operation between us, in a course of systematized & continued intellectual labour. It is now for *you* to decide. Do not attempt to make out to yourself or me that our principles entirely accord. They do *not*, nor *cannot*, at present (for people's views as I said are not to be altered in a moment).

'I wonder', she concluded diffidently, 'if you will choose to retain the lady fairy in your service or not?'

The letter had completely disarmed him, so he chose to retain the lady fairy in his service. On 9th September 1843 he wrote:

'I find it quite in vain to wait until I have leisure so I have resolved that I will leave all other things undone and set out for Ashley taking with me papers enough to enable me to forget this world and all its troubles and if possible its multitudinous charlatans—everything in short but the Enchantress of Number.

'My only impediment would be my Mother's health which is not at the moment quite as good as I could wish. Are you at Ashley? and is it still consistent with all your other arrangements that I should join you there? and will next Wednesday or Thursday or any other day suit you? and shall I leave the [illeg.] road at [illeg.] or at Bridgwater—and have you got Arbogast *Du Calcul Des Derivations* with you there (i.e. at Ashley)?

I shall bring some books about that horrible problem—the three bodies: which is almost as obscure as the existence of the celebrated book *De Tribes Importoribus*. So if you have Arbogast I will bring something else.

'Farewell my dear and much admired Interpretress.'

Because of the didactic tone of much of her previous letter she was much relieved by his reply, and wrote from Ashley Combe:

'My dear Babbage—On *Thursday* you will find the carriage at Minehead at the inn where the coach stops. We shall expect you to come by the train which leaves town between 7 & 8 in the morning (I think it is ½ after seven o'clock.)

'Your letter is *charming*, and Lord L. and I have smiled over it most approbatively. You must forgive me for showing it to him. It contains such *simple*, *honest*, *unfeigned* admiration for myself, that I could not resist giving *him* the pleasure of seeing it.

'I *have* Arbogast here, and a pretty ample collection besides for purposes of reference.

'I send you De Morgan's *kind and approving* letter about my article. I never expected that *he* would view my crude young composition so favourably.

'You must understand that I send you his letter in *strict confidence*. He might perhaps not like you to see his remarks about the *relative times* of the invention of the two engines. I am going to inform him of my grounds for feeling satisfied of the literal correctness of my statements on this point. I cannot say how much his letter pleased me.

'You are a brave man to give yourself wholly up to Fairy-guidance!—I advise you to allow yourself to be unresistingly bewitched, neck and crop, out and out, whole seas over, by that curious little being!'

He wrote even more ardently on 9th September:

My dear Lady Lovelace,

I enclose the letter of De Morgan.

I hope to be able to bring with me a final proof of the statement in which the dates of every part are clearly set out.

Charles Babbage, circa 1860, aged about seventy

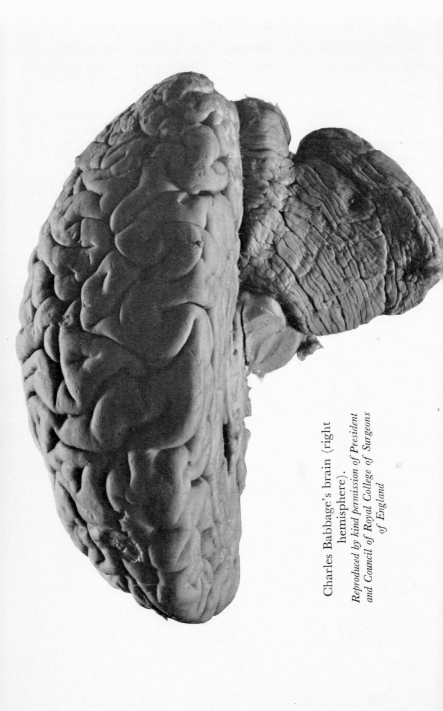

Charles Babbage's brain (right hemisphere).

Reproduced by kind permission of President and Council of Royal College of Surgeons of England

It is gratifying to me also for you know I had arrived at the same conclusion. You should have written an original paper.

The postponement of that will however only render it more perfect.

Many thanks for your itinerary and the assistant Engine at the last stage—I shall start for Bridgwater early on Thursday morning and supposing no impediment to coach &c. shall hope to reach you in the evening.

I have been making vast resolutions of unbounded work during my visit; but in preparing the materials I find indications of the necessity of repose after a long period of excitement.

Ever my fair Interpret*ress*,

Your faithful Slave

C. Babbage

22

The Book

*

*I*N 1844 Professor Augustus De Morgan wrote privately to
Lady Byron, saying that he had never told Lady Lovelace,
then twenty-eight, his opinion of her as a mathematician,
fearing that it would encourage her to engage in such intense
intellectual activity as to impair her health, never very strong.
He had therefore confined himself to saying 'Very good',
'Quite right' and so on. But he felt obliged to tell Lady Byron
that her daughter's power of thinking on abstract mathematical
and metaphysical questions was something so utterly out of
the ordinary for any beginner, man or woman, that it should be
very carefully considered; Lady Lovelace was obviously determined to try not only to reach but also to get beyond the
present bounds of knowledge, and if her mother thought that
it compared in intensity with the usual tastes of a young lady,
or if she thought that desire of distinction was the motive, and
science one of the many paths which might be chosen to obtain
it, then she did not know the whole. There was easily to be
seen the desire of distinction in Lady Lovelace's character,
but the mathematical bent was one which she must have taken
independently of that. Had any young beginner about to go to
Cambridge shown the same power, he would have prophesied
that the student's aptitude at grasping the strong points and
the real difficulties of first principles would certainly have made
him an original mathematical investigator, perhaps of first-
rate eminence.

'The tract about Babbage's machine is a pretty thing
enough, but I could I think produce a series of abstracts, out

of Lady Lovelace's first queries upon new subjects, which would make a mathematician see that it was no criterion of what might be expected from her', Professor De Morgan continued, adding with masculine condescension that all women mathematicians had shown knowledge and the power of getting it, but none, except perhaps (he spoke doubtfully) Maria Agnesi, had wrestled with difficulties and shown a man's strength in overcoming them. The reason, he said, was obvious: the very great tension of mind which they required was beyond the strength of a woman's physical power of application. Lady Lovelace had unquestionably as much power as would require all the strength of a man's constitution to bear the fatigue of thought to which it would undoubtedly lead her. It was all very well now, when the subject had not entirely engrossed her attention, but, later on, when, as always happened, the whole of the thoughts were continually and entirely concentrated upon them, the struggle between the mind and the body would begin.

'Perhaps you think that Lady Lovelace will, like Mrs. Somerville, go on in a course of regulated study, duly mixed with the enjoyment of society, the ordinary cares of life &c. But Mrs. Somerville's mind never led her into other than the *details* of mathematical work; Lady Lovelace will take quite a different route. It makes me smile', said Professor De Morgan complacently, 'to think of Mrs. Somerville's quiet acquiescence in ignorance of the nature of force, saying it is $\frac{dv}{dt}$ (a mathematical formula for it) "and that is all we know about the matter" —and to imagine Lady Lovelace reading this, much less writing it.'

Lady Lovelace's case was a peculiar one, he concluded, and having given the facts he left it to Lady Byron's better judgement to decide what to do, begging only that the note might be regarded as confidential.

In the event, the case was much more peculiar than Professor De Morgan imagined, for in spite of the proposition mentioned in Lady Lovelace's letter of 11th August 1843 nothing comparable with her notes on Menabrea's paper ever appears to have materialized. She may, on the other hand, have been referring in grandiloquent terms to what was actually to take place, an anticlimax of tragic magnitude. It was her own, her husband's and Charles Babbage's joint attempt to devise an infallible racing system. While a love of gambling was in Ada Lovelace's blood—she was, after all, her father's daughter—it seems inconceivable that Charles Babbage should have lent himself. It was, on the other hand, simply a variation of the theory of probability, or an extension of his own paper on *Some Questions connected with Games of Chance*; published more than twenty years before. He was, moreover, willing to try almost anything to raise money for the analytical engine, such as writing a three-volume novel and demonstrating a mechanical version of tit-tat-to, two projects which he envisaged but never carried out. It is also possible that he thought she had had a difficult life—as indeed she had, and could not help spoiling her, just as he had spoilt his 'little Georgiana'. There was, too, a well-known precedent in the case of Voltaire's mistress the Marquise de Châtelet, who gambled on mathematical probabilities. Whatever his reason, however, he was 'bewitched by fairy guidance' and agreed.

From 1844 onwards, until Lady Lovelace's death in 1852, at the age of thirty-six—the same age as her father, Lord Byron —the story devolves into lurid Victorian melodrama, ending in utter tragedy. Of this there is no indication in Charles Babbage's correspondence; for it seems that he destroyed all letters that would have been damaging to Lady Lovelace's reputation. It is, however, of some significance that in several of her letters to him, and in one or two of his to her, there are mysterious references to 'the book'—not any specific book, but 'the book'. This was contrary to their usual practice. Ordinarily if they mentioned a book they gave it its title. Had it occurred only once or twice it would hardly be worth mentioning, but it appeared more often, and sometimes the context is significant. It seems permissible, therefore, to assume that this was the code-word for the 'system'.

Otherwise, there is no indication for years of the double life Lady Lovelace was leading, or of the troubled waters beneath the surface of their pleasant social life, the London dinner parties, the country-house visits, the mutual and endearing interest in birds and dogs. There are long gaps in the correspondence, and it is difficult to believe that such a prolific correspondent as Lady Lovelace failed to fill them in. It seems clear that many letters were abstracted and destroyed.

Thus on a Monday in October 1844, she said: 'I cannot spare the book at all to-day, which I am very sorry for. At this moment I want it for constant reference, but I think you [can] have it *tomorrow*, & you could send it down to East Horsley by coach on Wednesday.' She mentioned it again in the same month: 'I am quite fully enjoying all this mess, but I will [send] you the *book directly*, & you can say, when you receive it, how long you will want to keep it.'

Charles, meanwhile, was much distressed by his mother's death on 5th December of that year. For several months there is a gap in the correspondence, and then, on 22nd August 1845, Lady Lovelace wrote to ask whether he 'would be so very kind as to see a gentleman (one of the Leighs) on Tuesday next at 11 o'clock, who wants to sell *me* a rifle & a pair of pistols which he declares to have been my father's.'

This was one of the sons of the Hon. Mrs. Augusta Leigh, her father's half-sister. He was in great distress and obliged to sell everything he had. Lady Lovelace had promised that nothing should be said of his circumstances, or application to herself. It would be a great favour if Charles would examine the articles and decide how far they were likely to be genuine and worth the price he might ask. She was ill again, adding in a postscript: 'Mr. *Hawkins* says there is nothing the least alarming.' And then, on 2nd September: 'I am recovering gradually and well; but have had a devil of a job. I hope I may be the better for it eventually.'

Again there is a gap of many months before she wrote, on 18th June 1846, about inviting the Countess Harley, a friend of Charles Babbage and General Menabrea, to dinner, fearing it would be a great liberty unless someone introduced her. And what was she to do about Baron B.? she enquired. There must have been something equivocal about the latter's position. Neither she nor Lord Lovelace had any objection to inviting him, she said, but would it get *her* into a scrape with her other lady guests, or with Society in general? 'In short I want to have five minutes' talk with you, but there is no time to lose, and that is the difficulty. I send you cards (of all kinds), and if you could leave them for us this afternoon, it would perhaps do. L. thought that *you*, being so great a friend of mine, might take upon yourself to chaperone me (or my cards) to Countess Harley, and to explain to her the strong wish of Lovelace and myself to make her acquaintance.'

Social difficulties were not the only ones in which Charles and Lady Lovelace found themselves in 1846. In that year the planet Neptune was discovered simultaneously by Adams and Leverrier, and a heated controversy arose from their conflicting claims. Charles, being as strongly inclined towards French science as he was disinclined towards that of Cambridge, supported the claim of Leverrier, hoping to induce the Royal Astronomical Society to award its medal to him. Sheepshanks was just as strongly in favour of Adams. In the event the medal was awarded to neither. All that came out of the controversy was the couplet:

'When Airy was told, he wouldn't believe it;
When Challis saw, he couldn't perceive it.'

Charles's firm conviction that nepotism outweighed merit was strengthened during this year of 1846. When the Mastership of the Mint became vacant he applied for it. It was a post which Newton had held and he therefore considered it worthy of a man of science. He intended to let his salary accumulate and then, with the £20,000 thus secured, at the end of ten or twelve years, construct the analytical engine. Unhappily, he was passed over in favour of a man named Sheil, who later became Minister at the Court of Tuscany.

In the same year an Act of Parliament was passed appointing commissioners for the supervision of the railways, for the growing number of accidents was causing great alarm. 'But I had no interest—a military engineer was appointed', said

Charles, full of self-pity, adding, when the situation was repeated a few years later: 'I am satisfied that in each of these cases the appointment was entirely due to family or political influence.'

He was to receive more comfort from his friend Charles Dickens about his recently published pamphlet on taxation.

Devonshire Terrace, 26 Feb. 1848

My dear Sir,

Pray let me thank you for your pamphlet. I confess that I am one of the inconvenient grumblers, and that I doubt the present or future existence of any Government in England strong enough to convert the people to your income tax principles, but I do not the less appreciate the ability with which you advocate them, nor am I the less gratified by any mark of your remembrance.

Faithfully yours always
Charles Dickens

And what the Lovelaces thought of him is more than usually discernible from a long letter, following a note on 27th August, with a postscript which may, or may not, be of significance: 'Bailliere & Maria Mason (the housemaid in Great Cumberland Place) have had orders to send parcels to you for me, tomorrow or Tuesday.'

Ashley Combe, 30 September 1848

Dear Babbage,

The skies are weeping unceasingly over your departure. The moment you went, it *set in* & it has scarcely intermitted for 10 minutes since.

You must have had a very wretched journey, you cannot think how we miss you; even the dogs, & the brace of thrushes (Sprite and Starry), look as if there was something wanting.

My *chief* reason for writing so soon is to mention that Lovelace has been really quite unhappy because he was unfortunately *just* too late to see you on Thursday morning. He rushed

after you to the lodge, & saw you *driving on. He* shouted,
Mrs. Court tried to run after the two Pegasi (!), the men on the
lawn & terrace (seeing there was something wrong), *all*
yelled and shouted, but in vain, neither you nor the beasts
would hear; tho' I really wonder that the *latter* did not run
away again, thro' the *fracas.* Lovelace is afraid you must think
he neglected you. How well we managed to effect Dunster
& that beautiful tour round the magnificent [illeg.] just
before hopeless wet set in! Were you so lucky to find Ryan on
your journey?

Sometimes I think *en passant* of all the *games*, & of notations
for them. If any good idea should accidentally strike me, I will
take care to mention it to you. But this is not likely. I believe
the Molesworths will come here on the 10th October for a
day or two. I am very anxious to hear from you.

Ever yours, A. A. Lovelace

P.S. The *nightingales* say you must write to them, but as you
can't sing, & hate music, I wonder how you will manage to
send them any intelligible song!

In *The Athenaeum* for 14th October 1848 Professor De
Morgan, reviewing Weld's *History of the Royal Society*, defended
Charles Babbage over the Government's refusal to let him
continue with the difference engine after 1842. De Morgan
felt that the public had a right to an explanation from the
Government, Sir Robert Peel having turned it off with a joke
in the House of Commons, recommending that the machine
should be set to calculate the time at which it would be of use.
'He ought rather to have advised that it *should* be set to compute the number of applications which might remain un-
answered before a Minister, if the subject were not one which
might affect his Parliamentary power. If it had done this, it
would have shown that its usefulness would have commenced.'
On this Lady Lovelace made a pertinent comment in her
next letter, and also enquired about Charles's scheme for
making an automaton to play tit-tat-to, or noughts and crosses.
In carrying out the initial research, he found that every game

of skill was susceptible of being played by an automaton, and that in tit-tat-to a comparatively insignificant number of combinations was required for all the possible moves and situations. He soon sketched out the mechanism, envisaging taking the machine on tour, the proceeds to be used to construct the analytical engine. It was to be designed for children, with the figures of two children playing one against the other, accompanied by a lamb and a cock, the winner to clap his hands as the cock crowed, the loser to cry as the lamb bleated. It would have illustrated the best definitions of chance, he said, by the philosopher and the poet:

'Chance is but the expression of man's ignorance'
Laplace

'All chance, design ill understood'
Pope

On further enquiry, however, he found that by the time the automaton was built it would be too late to use the money for the analytical engine, and that in any case the most popular exhibition was that of the little dwarf, General Tom Thumb.

'I hope you got Lovelace's packet, (& also a subsequent letter *from the Birds*). The *Life Preserver* is safe here. What shall I do with it? It certainly can't go by *post* (until there is a yet further extension of the postal *system*).

'I hope *you* are as pleased as *I* am with the account of you and your engines, in the last Athenaeum. *We* think it very just and impartial—let the Government answer it, if they can. I am vexed to think of your returning to unwholesome, *dull* London. Do *frequent* us a little more, at Horsley, which is come-atable. You say nothing of tit-tat-to in your last. I am alarmed lest it should never be *accomplished*. I want you to *complete* something; especially if the something is likely to produce silver and golden somethings . . .

'Write to me again directly, or the *Birds* will be angry, & won't sing. Sirius [a dog] is becoming a little steadier; but do what he will, he continues the *universal* favourite. Nelson hates him worse than ever.

'I have much more to say, but I hear the fatal horn which (like death) waits nobody's pleasure.'

She wrote again from Ashley Combe on 2nd November 1848, to say that she had seen with great concern the death of Mrs. Dawson Damer at St. Leonards, and thought he had lost a good friend. Had he noticed the account (in the *Athenaeum* of the 21st October) of the American astronomer Mitchell? she enquired. It was very interesting, and there was in it a good remark about science never having been over-patronized by Royalty.

She was to leave the following Wednesday for Leicester-shire for a few days. She did not know what to do about the Transit—and did not wish to lose it. It seemed it was at a convenient hour enough, eleven o'clock in the morning. But they had no contrivances at Ashley. She supposed one could see it with the naked eye (through smoked glass). Any direc-tions he could send would be valuable.

She then spoke about her young son Ralph, now nine years old, who had been adopted by his grandmother Lady Noel Byron, and made by her her principal heir. His mother had had two or three more letters from him, 'really *very* promising, & showing much accurate habit of observation, & *excellent sense*, too; also a facility for *caricaturing*, which is quite a *talent*, but which is doubtless one of some danger. He is, however, I suspect, the *tortoise* who will get before the *hares* by & bye.'

She concluded, with a sly dig at Charles:

' "Sirius" has been obliged to submit to a *muzzle*, whenever he goes on expeditions; he pertinaciously attacked the *Gallinacea*, but he is everybody's favourite, and wins all hearts, from the stern *Earl's* (his master) downwards, always well received and made much of! Old "Nelson" has ceased *active* interference with his son, & looks *philosophical* & *saturnine*, but pays great court to me. Nelson will always be *judicious*.'

Charles Babbage, like Lord Byron and Lady Lovelace, was addicted to parrots, and wrote on one occasion of 'a fair young creature' who had arrived in his household, who sat every morning at his side at the breakfast table, and let him know in the evening when it was time to retire by saying: 'Polly wants to go to bed', and then he rang for his servant to carry the cage away.

Lady Lovelace enquired, before racing on about one of the dogs:

'How is *Polly*? Conceive my maid being so mad as to petition taking *Sirius* (on a pleasure expedition) to *Leicestershire!* Imagine the bother we should have with that spotted scamp, at *inns*, *stations*, etc.; not to mention the (almost) *certainty* of his killing Mrs. *Noel's* fowls, & playing the very deuce *there*. But I believe May thinks the dog more wonderful & perfect than ever!'

As he grew older Charles Babbage became more and more careless about letters and dates. On 7th November 1848 Lady Lovelace wrote:

Minehead, 7 Nov. 1848

Dear Babbage,

I am surprised at having no answer to my letter to you of last week, in which I asked about the *Transit*.

Now my address will be (until after this week) Peckleton House, Hinkley, Leicestershire.

I really half fear you are *ill*. I want you to come down to Horsley on Saturday the 18th of this month.

In haste,

Yours very indignantly,

A. A. Lovelace

And, again, on 12th November:

Peckleton, 12 Nov. 1848

Dear Babbage,

I have not yet succeeded in getting you to comprehend that *you* were asked for the *18th*, Ryan for the *25th*.

Why you have confounded the *two together* I cannot imagine! We hold *you* to the 18th, but if you like to come on the *25th* also, DO.

What a puzzle-pated old phil. you are!
I explained it clearly in my first note. Why did you *jumble* it?
(Unsigned)

Eight days later he wrote a cryptic note, which suggests that he was acting as intermediary between Lady Lovelace and the bookmakers. It was, of course, essential that someone should act in this capacity. No lady at this period, and certainly no peeress, could possibly have had direct dealings with them. The strict conventions of the day are sufficiently revealed by the fact that her translation of Menabrea's paper and notes were published anonymously.

My dear Lady Lovelace,
    Your letters were posted in proper time.
    By force of Rail, Cab and busses I reached Mrs. Griffiths and got no news, only the address at Plaistow.
    Mr. G. advised my enquiring in Moorgate St. This carried me back into the City.
    I then posted (re-addressed) your letters and left word (written down) in Moorgate St. your directions about Wednesday.
    I then went to Messrs. [illeg.] the bird fancier who advised Mr. Williams of Oxford St. to stuff the bird. I had a conference with the latter, who is to follow your directions and in about ten days it will be ready.
    In three days I am to be informed as to the cause of death which the fancier thinks arises from over feeding.
                                        Ever truly yours
                                        C. Babbage
10 p.m. Monday 20 Nov. 1848.

His next note was innocuous enough:

My dear Lady Lovelace,
    I conclude that your visit is not to London and therefore I shall not see you before Saturday next.

As far as the Engine is concerned this is a gain but personally it is a loss.

The complaint of the poor bird was inflammation of the stomach. In all other respects it was in perfect health and very fat. It will I presume be ready in about a week.

I am going to visit the starling to-day and shall invite it here as a friend of yours.

Polly will of course be jealous but I shall take care not to let the rivals approach each other.

Tomorrow the R. Society are to hold their debate. I go simply to see the turn-out.

Ever sincerely yours
C. Babbage

Dorset St., 29 Nov. 1848.

Then, on 4th December 1848, he said: 'Not having heard from you today I infer that tomorrow will bring me a note. I have an engagement for Wednesday which will prevent me from attending to your wishes about the book.'

On the 17th she wrote from Horsley: 'The *starling* don't talk as yet. I hope you will come next Saturday.' Two days later, after begging him to stay for a few days over Christmas and have 'a little holiday', she said: 'I hope to send you either tomorrow evening or Thursday morning a *book* which I think will interest you.' She concluded by remarking that her ten-year-old daughter, Lady Anne King, known in the family as Annabella, was staying with her grandmother, Lady Noel-Byron, at Brighton, from whence had come an unsatisfactory account of the state of the child's lungs. 'She went there a week ago, having had a nasty enough cough & cold (like so many others). But *two* doctors there say the lungs are affected, & that if great care is not taken, there will be elements of future organic disease.' This gloomy prediction was not fulfilled. Lady Anne grew up and lived to a ripe old age.

Birds were again the topic of Lady Lovelace's next letter, dated 8th February 1849.

'The parrot here has made an excursion, it had been allowed to sit at the *open* window, & even to walk on the *leads*, &

then great amazement was felt at its *disappearance* one day! It was found, after two days. I suppose it will disappear again by & bye. The starling is not (yet) lost. I am thought a very unreasonable person, for my comments upon these matters. I have no confidence in *winged* things remaining stationary.'

This was followed up by a note on 11th February: 'I will send the *book* on Tuesday, & it can be left with you till Friday, I believe.' What she said in her next may also have had bearing on the book: 'I *do* settle in Town on *Thursday*. I hope what I *wrote* out for you was intelligible. I wrote in a *hurry*, but I think it was *plain* & *definite*, tho' somewhat of a *scrawl* (calligraphically).'

Charles Dickens gave a dinner party on 24th March 1849, at which Lord and Lady Lovelace and Charles Babbage were guests. ' . . . few had a greater warmth of admiration for Dickens than Lord Byron's "Ada" ', said John Forster, 'on whom Paul Dombey's death laid a strange fascination.'

In her next letter, dated 20th September 1849, from East Horsley, she had a sly dig at the Duke and Duchess of Somerset, with whom Charles had been on terms of intimate friendship for many years. And she also mentioned the book:

'We propose to be down at Ashley on Thursday next—this day week, & both L. & I agree in urging you to come *there* during Oct. as the best possible rest & refreshment for you. Our home is not like the *Somerset* house, & I think we are now more regular even than we ever were.

'You can have a pony all to yourself, & never need walk a step except on the terrace, the *"philosopher's walk"*. I propose to sleep in *Town* on Wednesday next, & go down by express train on Thursday. Will *you* come back and go *with* me?

'Don't forget the *new course* [cover?] you promised to bring *for the book*. The poor book is very shabby, & wants one.

'There is a great deal I want to explain to you *which can't be by letter*. I can't decipher satisfactorily some *indications* in the work in question.'

Lady Lovelace added that she had heard from the thirteen-year-old Lord Ockham, now in the Royal Navy. His letter had come via Holland; of a date fifteen days earlier than a letter from the equator. 'On July 26th', she said, 'the *Swift* took a Dutch barque off Bruna (one of the Cape de Verdes). All *well & merry*, & the letter is a very charming one.'

On 28th September she was writing from Ashley Combe begging him to pay a visit—at present coaches were running daily both from Bridgwater and from Taunton to Porlock, but she thought that they would continue to do so only for about a fortnight longer. But he would be with them long before that, she hoped, adding that it was the express train (9.50, Paddington Station) which met the coaches.

She then referred once again to a 'package', and then to the book:

'We must ask you to do us the favour of bringing down a package; & also of going to Great Cumberland Street to select some things which *Lovelace* wants out of a *parcel* which is there. Of all this I will [write] to you fully, in a day or two, & will take care so to arrange it as to give you the *least possible* trouble.

'I was so hurried & bothered the evening you came (not expecting you in the least) that I could scarcely speak to you, yet I was *particularly* glad to see you, even in that uncomfortable way & it was a *very* good thing as regarded the *book*.

'I think your visit to Paris has been a most excellent step; & very pleasant. I hope you will soon come to people 'the Philosopher's walk'.

'Don't forget to pay respects to *Pearce* en passant, & pray enquire after his (young) '*Nelson*'. He was an own brother of Rover's, one of Flora's *first* litter, & it has turned out *splendid*, the *best* of the lot, in fact! It is called "Nelson" (Junior), & it is very like *Papa*.'

Charles meanwhile had sent Thackeray a copy of the *Ninth Bridgewater Treatise*, the latter hoping to thank him 'for much instructive and pleasant reading, when I go with your book in my carpet bag for a little country holiday'.

The only open reference to Lady Lovelace's interest in racing was made in Charles's next letter in the autumn of 1850, in which he also mentioned the Earl of Rosse, President of the Royal Society and a noted amateur astronomer.

My dear Lady Lovelace,

I fear some letters of mine must have been delayed in Dorset Street as I have not heard of your movements since we parted. I now find by the papers that you were at Doncaster on the triumph of Voltigeur. As I return in a few days I hope to see you before your trip to the West. I was very much pleased with the [illeg.] bridge on which I spent a day. I met Lord Fitz-william and his daughter at Bangor with whom I travelled to Dublin having fair calm weather and pleasant company. Having seen Sir Wm. Hamilton I went on to Ld. Rosse from whom I have just parted.

We had only five nights of observing and very bad definition owing to the East wind. I saw however many nebulæ also Neptune and possibly one of the satellites.

I was very much pleased with the whole establishment for making and using the telescope. I am going to Manchester today and on Wednesday shall possibly go on to Lord Hather-ton's near Wolverhampton, returning the next day or on Friday to London.

Pray let me have a line in Dorset St. on my arrival. I am anxious to get at work again for I have done nothing. I shall surely be able to reach Ashley this year as I have promised to go to Wentworth in October.

Ever sincerely yours
C. Babbage

Liverpool, Sunday, 22 Sept. 1850

23

The Coronet, Slightly Tarnished

*

*T*HE tragedy was drawing rapidly and inexorably to its close. Lady Lovelace's double life was coming to a sad and sinister end.

On 1st November 1850 she wrote to Charles Babbage from Ashley Combe a letter which, by reason of the reference to getting a livelihood, seems to refer to someone other than herself, but it could, just as easily, have been a deliberate mystification designed, like 'the book', to conceal her racing activities and specifically, in this instance, her losses. The reference to 'the invalid' may well have been to herself and the onset of the internal cancerous growth from which she was to die two years hence.

Ashley, Friday 1 Nov. 1850

Dear Babbage,

I have delayed writing, intending to send you a *long* letter. I have not time to do this yet, so I had better delay no longer letting you know the invalid is certainly *better*, from Erasmus Wilson's medicines; but the health is so utterly broken at present, that I wish to follow the plan you suggest; & to have the examination & enquiries by *your* medical friend, as soon as return to Town shall admit of it.

I think this of great importance. Some very thorough remedial measures must be pursued or all power of getting any livelihood in *any* way whatsoever will be at an end.

Yours in haste

A.L.

Whether or not the references were to herself, the infallible system, worked out with such meticulous precision by two of the greatest mathematical geniuses of the age, or, indeed, of any age, and with the aid of the analytical engine, had by this time proved, or was proving, hopelessly fallible. The vagaries of horses and jockeys and the many imponderables were defeating them.

Lord Lovelace, who, intellectually, was out of his depth with both of them, was strong-minded enough to retire at an early date and cut his losses, expecting his wife to do the same. Lady Lovelace, however, possessed by a mania to perfect the system, continued without his knowledge, and was aided and abetted to some extent by Charles Babbage, who was probably unaware of the full horrors of the situation into which she was getting herself.

On the 13th May of what was probably 1851 Charles asked Lady Lovelace:

'What are your commands for the day? I am going into the City and return to dinner at home unless you wish otherwise. . . . Let me know that you have passed a good night. Don't bore yourself with writing, a verbal answer by my messenger or a visit from your own Lady-bird will be sufficient.'

In his next, undated, note he referred again to the practice of sending her maid, evolved for her convenience while she was lying ill at Great Cumberland Place.

My dear Lady Lovelace,

I sat last night reading the advertisements of deserted wifes [*sic*] to charm back their wandering Lords.

I am not a wanderer though I had none to charm.

Tomorrow an American breakfasts with me, an Italian joins him, an undertaker then comes to me on business, finally I might go to a sale to bid for a [illeg.] so that I am tolerably employed until the evening when I am engaged to dine with your neighbour in Park Lane. If however you should send a messenger I will give orders to admit her to the Drawing room and I can spare time to make any arrangements which may be desirable.

I am ever truly yours

Tues. evening.   C. Babbage

He was her confidant in many of the things that were taking place, but not, it seems, in all, until the end. There are equivocal passages in two of her letters to him, showing that as early as 1843 she was not impervious to masculine charms if a love of racing were among them.

On 6th July 1843 she had told Charles that a John Knight had reappeared from Holland and they had spent a delightful morning together. 'I see I am more his ladye-love than ever', she said. 'He is an excellent creature and deserves to have a nice ladye-love.' A few days later, on 13th July, she sent him a note from John Knight, saying:

'It will show you the tone of writing between us; & the sort of footing we are on. Are you not amused at "Your Ladyship"? which just means, by the way, that I am anything but *my Ladyship* to him! Am I very naughty to send you such a caller up of many & dubious speculations? No!'

And on 2nd September 1845 she mentioned a John Crosse, who was known to Charles Babbage and had written an article in *The Westminster*. Was he the same Crosse who caused so much trouble at the end? There is a strange similarity in the unusual way of spelling Crosse.

At some point Charles Babbage had transferred to Lady Lovelace's service one of his own servants, named Mary Wilson. She may have been his cook, in which case, being a gourmet, he made a considerable sacrifice. Mary Wilson acted as intermediary between Lady Lovelace and the outside world, including the bookmakers.

The secret came out in the summer of 1852. Lady Lovelace was in the worst stages of her illness; mattresses had been placed on the walls and floor of her room so that when she threw herself about in her agony she would not injure herself. Between bouts of this indescribable pain she was at last compelled to confess everything to her husband: that she had twice pawned his family jewels and had twice asked her mother, Lady Noel Byron, to redeem them, the latter not only doing so but also keeping her daughter's secret. Among the other disasters which Lady Lovelace revealed was the fact that she was in the 'toils of an unscrupulous gang of betting men', who were not above blackmailing and threatening to reveal her activities to the world.

Saddening and embittering though it must have been to Lord Lovelace, one would have more sympathy for him if he had not kept his own early participation out of Lady Noel Byron's ken, or failed to include his own betting debts when a supposed full statement of financial difficulties had been made to her. He thus resented being under any obligation whatever to his mother-in-law, while she, on her part, was horrified to find that he was not the restraining influence on her daughter which she had believed him to be. Although she perforce lived as his guest during the last stages of her daughter's illness, neither was ever again on friendly terms with the other.

But they agreed that Mary Wilson, who knew too much, should go, or, at least, the dominating Lady Noel Byron decided and he agreed, for in the presence of both of them Lady Noel Byron discharged her, Lady Lovelace piteously desiring that a promise of hers made to Charles, to pay Mary Wilson £100 in case of dismissal, should be made good by her mother. Lady Noel Byron eventually carried out this promise, as will be seen, but with a very bad grace.

Just as, in her distress over the jewels, Lady Lovelace had turned to her mother, she now turned to Charles Babbage, the father figure, to whom once, in a trivial note, she had signed herself 'Yours filially'. He responded at once. His 'dear and much admired interpretress', his 'enchantress of number', was in dire trouble. This was enough for him. This eccentric, forgetful, choleric, misguided but honourable man of sixty-one went immediately to Great Cumberland Place and was shown into the sick-room, where there was a brief, painful interview. The dying woman begged him to be her executor, and placed various papers in his hands. The love and esteem in which she held him can be judged from the next letter, which was, in effect, her last will and testament. And in her remorse it seems that she desired that the £600 on her insurance policy, together with any other available funds, should buy back compromising letters held by the mysterious Crosse:

August 12th, 1852
6 Gt. Cumberland Place

Dear Babbage,

In the event of my sudden decease before the completion of a will I write you this letter to entreat that you will *as my Executor* attend to the following directions:

1^stly. You will apply to my Mother for the sum of £600; to be employed by you as I have elsewhere privately directed you.

2^ndly. You will go to my bankers, Messrs. Drummonds and obtain from them my account and Balance (if any) and also all my *old Drafts*.

3^rdly. You will dispose of all papers and property deposited by me with you, as you may think proper *after full examination*.

Any *balance* in money at my Banker's you will add to the £600 above named to be similarly employed.

In the fullest reliance on y^r. faithful performance of the above, I am

Most sincerely & affectionately Yours
Augusta Ada Lovelace

And in the same envelope was a slip of paper on which was written in pencil:

Dear Babbage,

I think the enclosed will *do* as a makeshift.

But I suppose I ought to write a (sealed-up) letter to Messrs. Drummonds in case of my decease, for you to keep and present to them. I send you a rough copy of what I propose.

This was the rough draft of the note to Messrs. Drummond:
Gentlemen,

Charles Babbage Esq. of 1 Dorset St. etc. presents to you this letter (with my seal unbroken). Will you be so good as to deliver to him immediately whatever balance I may have at your Bank—and likewise all my *old* cheques and my account up to the day of delivery of this letter.

Yours &c.

Already indignant about Mary Wilson, whom he believed to have been unjustly dismissed and against Lady Lovelace's wishes, Charles was cut to the heart by the desperate situation of his adored lady fairy. He read the papers and, choking back his rage and emotion, explained that the direction to apply to Lady Noel Byron could have no effect unless she chose to comply with it, adding that the application to Drummonds would not only be improper but would also, so far as he knew, be illegal without the sanction of Lord Lovelace. To this in her weakness she expressed in the fewest words her most unhesitating conviction that both her mother and her husband would comply with her last wishes.

Charles then entreated her to put on paper, in words however short, her private direction to him as to the distribution of the money. Then, legal or not, for he could do nothing else, he took the papers.

Lord Lovelace, meanwhile, was trying to make some sense out of the net in which his wife had entangled herself, and to find a way of preventing 'the scoundrels' (as they were always named in the correspondence) from molesting her even as she lay dying. In this he was helped by Woronzow Greig, the barrister son of Mary Somerville by her first husband, who had been with him at Trinity College, Cambridge.

In the same house, though presumably not on speaking terms with him, and within a few hours of her daughter's death, the unimaginative and unemotional Lady Noel Byron noted: 'I write in the hearing of her groans, and of the little Bullfinch singing carelessly his wonted airs. In the next room one whose feelings are far from [being] in harmony with mine.'

As if this were not tragedy enough, the fifteen-year-old Lord Ockham, distressed by his mother's illness and resentful of the iron discipline of the Royal Navy, ran away and joined the Merchant Service. He was eventually found, at Liverpool, but, after other vicissitudes, insisted on leading his own life, living as a poor man among the poor, and dying of consumption at the age of twenty-six.

Such was her remorse on her deathbed that Lady Lovelace

implored her mother to have inscribed on a cenotaph at Kirkby Mallory Hall the following words, 'to recall her memory':

'And the prayer of faith shall save the sick,
And the Lord shall raise him up;
And if he have committed sins,
They shall be forgiven him.'

She died on 27th November 1852. Two years before, while on a visit to Newstead Abbey with her husband, she had heard a different version of the Byron story and had for many months been estranged from her mother, expressing the wish, from which she never deviated, to be buried beside her father in the Byron Vault at Hucknall Torkard Church in Nottinghamshire. This wish was carried out on 3rd December, when the vault was closed.

The Byron Vault dates from 1638, when the wife of Sir John Byron was laid to rest there, and with the permission of the Home Office, and the approval of the Rev. Lord Byron, was reopened nearly eighty-six years later on 15th June 1938. There the coffins of father and daughter, both thirty-six years of age, were found to lie side by side, within a foot of each other, the poet and the mathematician, geniuses both. At the head of each coffin was its owner's coronet, symbol of temporal power. Lady Lovelace's was in a better condition than her father's, consisting originally of an upper rim, surmounted by eight points, each bearing a pearl, and, alternating with the latter, on the lower rim, a similar number of strawberry leaves. The crimson velvet cap, lined with ermine, originally within the coronet and surrounded by a gold tassel, had perished, but parts of the ermine remained.

Her coronet was only slightly tarnished. Without her mother's skill and adroitness in dealing with Charles Babbage, the lawyers and others, her reputation to her contemporaries might have been much worse.

She had not been in the vault for more than ten days when Charles Babbage received a letter from Lady Noel Byron's solicitors, Wharton & Ford, saying that directions had been given that all engagements depending upon Lady Lovelace's word should be fulfilled. In case he knew of anyone of whom she may have thought, would he be good enough to favour them with a statement of such intent on her part.

On the 19th December 1852 Charles Babbage replied, enclosing copies of 'the only testamentary papers of the late Lady Lovelace which Mr. Babbage is at present aware he possesses'. His somewhat ungracious reply indicates that he was already suspicious of his old friend Lady Noel Byron, and resented what she was saying about Mary Wilson, from whom he had heard a great deal. This suspicion is confirmed by his next note to the solicitor. He wished Lady Noel Byron to be informed that he would willingly enter upon a full explanation with Dr. Lushington of all that was known and said by the late Countess of Lovelace relating to Miss Wilson, as well as her wishes respecting other persons. Dr. Lushington had acted for Lady Byron as confidential adviser in the separation proceedings, and on his 'judgment and high sense of honor' Charles said that he placed implicit confidence.

Dr. Lushington, however, at Lady Noel Byron's request, refused to see Charles personally, though he wrote a non-committal 'paper', said the solicitor, after he was acquainted with all that had passed with Mr. Babbage relating to Miss Wilson. Charles was thereupon very angry and declined all further communication with them about this paper. He asked the solicitor to inform Lady Noel Byron that he was convinced that Dr. Lushington had not a full knowledge of all that was known and said by the late Lady Lovelace relating to Miss Wilson, and it was his opinion that no correct conclusion could be arrived at on the subject unless he put Dr. Lushington in possession of all that was known. If this was not desired by Lady Noel Bryon then he did not wish to interfere further in the matter.

It was not desired by Lady Noel Byron. She told the solicitor that she thought 'great caution necessary with Mr. Babbage', and suggested a modification in what he proposed to write to him. She was also doubtful about the expediency of bringing Dr. Lushington into the business at present, adding 'a precaution about Miss Wilson, for she, too, must be required to sign a few words'. She was glad the other servants had signed.

Charles had meanwhile delivered to the solicitor a package of papers, which was sent at once to Lady Noel Byron, 'who, of course, will not part with any receipts or bills of her daughter, the late Lady Lovelace, whether they were made in the names of Mrs. or Miss Wilson and Mrs. or Miss Taylor'. The solicitors held Lady Noel Byron's cheque for £100 to Miss Wilson. Before delivering it it was necessary for them to have an interview. Interfering yet again, Lady Noel Byron thought the terms of one of the solicitor's letters to Charles Babbage 'dangerous', as they seemed to promise on her part that she should fulfil whatever he might expect to have been Lady Lovelace's engagements.

The paper eventually contrived by Lady Noel Byron and approved by Dr. Lushington was dated 5th January 1853. It was to be read by Mary Wilson and signed by her as having been read. It was as follows:

'At the time when Lady Lovelace thought it right that Miss Mary Wilson should quit her service and when Lady Noel Byron did in consequence with the sanction of Lord Lovelace, and in his presence, discharge Miss Mary Wilson, Lady Lovelace also specially desired that a promise of hers should be made good by Lady Noel Byron. That promise had been made not to Miss Mary Wilson herself but to Mr. Babbage through whose recommendation chiefly Lady Lovelace had taken Miss Mary Wilson into her service and it was to this effect that if Miss Wilson should be dismissed £100 should be given her as a compensation for the prospects she had relinquished to enter Lady Lovelace's service.

'Lady Noel Byron fulfils Lady Lovelace's engagement irrespective of the merits or demerits of Miss Mary Wilson.'

But this was not the end of Charles Babbage's part in the affair. Feeling that the truth was being suppressed, he made himself as difficult and unpleasant as possible, demanding, at one point, the return of all his letters. This was acceded to eventually, and later on he must have destroyed them, for they have vanished from all the obvious places. Some glimpses of what he was doing are shown in Lady Noel Byron's correspondence.

Writing on 5th February 1853 to her friend the Rev. Frederick William Robertson, of Brighton, the popular preacher, she was, as usual, fully convinced of her rectitude, and utterly incapable of seeing anyone else's point of view but her own. She was also, as always, unable to understand the whims and vagaries of genius. In justice to her, however, she may, considering the nature of her daughter's illness and behaviour, have found it absolutely necessary to place Lady Lovelace under some kind of restraint, which Charles, who was often misguided in his zeal and his hatred, may have exaggerated.

When she was forced into positions of antagonism one of the greatest pains she suffered, and the least understood, was the suppression of kind feelings, said Lady Noel Byron to Robertson. She was sorry, even grieved, for those who were suffering from 'false visions of relative facts, or from internal warfare', that she longed to express sympathy, and yet her own cause (which she supposed to be that of truth) would be damaged, as people thought, by her doing so. Was there no way of reconciling the want to be kind with the duty to be true?

'I feel this very strongly about poor B. I know intuitively that his passions and his better nature are tearing him to pieces. Is there no voice to say to him—"Be still"? It is very hard to be misrepresented by those who act for one, though I cannot say it is without my sanction, seeing no other course open. I do not believe that you or any friend of mine can enter fully into this part of my troubles.'

'Poor B.', however, whipped up by the indignant Mary Wilson, who had told him, perhaps also with some exaggeration, the secrets of the sick-room, had decided to write a memoir about the actual or supposed ill treatment of his poor lady fairy. In this he intended to show that she was under restraint from some day in August 1852. This must have given Lady Noel Byron some uneasy moments, for he suggested it to John Murray, the publisher, who was no friend of hers, having published for Byron and taken his part throughout the separation proceedings and afterwards. Fortunately for her, and fortunately, perhaps, for Charles Babbage, though not for posterity, this was yet another of his ventures which never saw the light of day. Murray either took alarm, thinking it would implicate living people, or else considered it in bad taste, or both, for the book, if it was ever written, never came out.

'I hear that he was much reprobated, for his intention of writing a memoir, in the Murray circle, which had no contact with mine', said Lady Noel Byron to Robertson on 13th February 1853.

Someone else seems to have taken fright. Robertson said to Lady Noel Byron on 22nd March: 'Your account of the recalcitration of Mr. B.'s friend from the task of mediation is inexplicable, but I am glad his own circle disapprove of the intention of the memoir.' And he added four days later: 'I have little doubt that fear is the solution of B.'s conduct, and I do not feel that his interest in Miss W. is altogether of a disinterested character. It is too deep and pertinacious to be so accounted for.'

Lady Noel Byron had evidently thought of publicly contradicting both Charles Babbage and the things said about her by Mary Wilson, for he added:

'Nor have I any doubt respecting the necessity of what you propose in reference to Miss W. for your own defence. I think the defence *does* matter: for I find more and more that character cannot be left to take care of itself. Silence is supposed to give consent. A contradiction at least makes the world feel that there is another side to the story. Two things, however, will need to be guarded against in putting such a defence on paper.

'1. To keep clear of any accusation which is actionable at law. Facts, such as police warnings and the entertainment of gentlemen in the house, if easily substantiated, should be named: but no more, I think.

'2. To leave as little as possible dependent upon the sagacity of the reader. The extreme into which you are most tempted to fall is exactly the opposite of that which ladies generally are exposed to, and is accountable for by the fact that you have so often to write what was to be understood by the initiated, not others, conciseness and an *esoteric* way of writing— I believe I could with safety show all the letters I ever received from you, and no one would make out anything in shape and colour from them. Of course this is right under such circumstances: but in a composition which is to convey its whole import to the densest reader, it will require some care to avoid the results of long habit.

'But I certainly would not delay doing this. You owe it to yourself and to all your friends to do it. B. thinks that you will be silent, knowing that you have a secret. Any disposition shown to publish all if necessary would most probably moderate his tone.'

When Charles Babbage eventually withdrew, Lady Noel Byron apparently did the same, although another of her friends, Anna Jameson, the Quaker writer, tried to mediate, for she said that the opinion generally entertained of Charles was that he was 'perfectly honest and honourable, but betrayed by temper into all kinds of extravagancies in word and deed'. She had been asked by third parties to see him and hear *his* version, but had declined at present, as she felt great repugnance towards it, but would not shrink if necessary from listening to him or expressing her own opinion on certain points, but it would do no good at present. Sometimes the wish came across her to look the man in the face and say: 'Thus didst thou.' If it were fitting, however, there would come a time.

Robertson, a few days later, was as puzzled as the modern reader. 'How can your position be made less favourable by others' indecision?' he asked Lady Noel Byron. 'I am perplexed by attempts to guess. That B's conduct was the result of design I had made up my mind to believe.' And he concluded: 'Could you trust B's letters by post? I hope you have not forgotten my offer to transcribe any that could not be safely confided to an amanuensis.'

She evidently corrected him, for a few days later, on 9th April, he wrote again, saying that her letter contained nothing that surprised him. And in his reference to 'hush money' he meant presumably the £100 intended for Mary Wilson.

'Your letter contained nothing that surprised me—B's relation to Miss W. I had been some time convinced of—the *appearance* of hush money is unfortunate, but as you are quite clear of it, no permanent harm can result. By permanent I mean spiritual: for it is poetical and not the actual Divine justice which leads us to expect to find honesty the best policy and innocence rewarded, the good happified and the bad found out at the end of life's play.'

The Babbage-Lovelace story ends here in the extant correspondence, although Charles was undoubtedly well aware of all that was taking place.

Dr. Lushington, for example, had advised the solicitor to enquire of the Law & Equity Insurance office about the policy on Lady Lovelace's life with a view to ascertaining the particulars and whether other applications had been made. And Woronzow Greig had told Dr. Lushington of 'the additional act of treachery' perpetrated by the delivery of Lord Lovelace's confidential letter to the 'ruffian who is now causing so much vexation'. He was hoping to find out details of the sum claimed by Crosse. Later, Greig, Lushington, Lord Lovelace and a lawyer named Karslake compromised with Crosse by the policy on Lady Lovelace's life to obtain letters from him. In April 1852 they were still negotiating with him. This, said Greig to Lushington, was for the destruction of all Lady Lovelace's letters and all her husband's, including 'the all-important letter from him to her, assenting to and authorizing her betting proceedings, and which letter she had handed over to Crosse'. Crosse agreed that all such letters should be destroyed in Karslake's presence, on condition that Lord Lovelace's claim under the policy should be withdrawn. This was excellent, as far as it went, but he also required that Karslake should write him a letter on behalf of Lord Lovelace, Lady Noel Byron and their friends exonerating him from all blame in the racing transactions in which he had been engaged with Lady Lovelace. This they were not prepared to do.

Was it, then, the mysterious Crosse to whom Lady Lovelace had privately directed Charles Babbage to pay such money as she possessed? Almost certainly it was, but Charles's secret seems to have gone with him to the grave. It is of some significance, however, that apart from his three sons the only beneficiary under his own will, dated 13th October 1871, was Mary Wilson, who received £3 a month free of tax for life.

Part Four
(1852–1871)

*

How much has happened in these fifty years—a period more remarkable than any, I will continue to say, in the annals of mankind. I am not thinking of the rise and fall of Empires, the change of dynasties, the establishment of governments. I am thinking of those revolutions of science which have had much more effect than any political causes, which have changed the position and prospects of mankind more than all the conquests and all the codes, and all the legislators that ever lived.

BENJAMIN DISRAELI, 1873. Quoted by
O. J. HOWARTH, *The British Association*, 1922

24

A Bore with Extraordinary Talents

*

*H*AVING mastered the subject of the analytical engine by 1848, Charles Babbage decided to make a complete set of drawings for what he named Difference Engine No. 2. This was an improved version of the first, incorporating many of the simplified devices used in the analytical engine. Four years later his friend the Earl of Rosse (ancestor of the present peer, who married the mother of Lord Snowdon) had become President of the Royal Society, and in this capacity asked Charles whether he was willing to give them to the Government if the latter would have the machine constructed.

'My feeling was, after the sad sacrifice of the past, that I ought not to think of sacrificing any further portion of my life upon the subject', said Charles. 'If, however, they chose to have the difference engine made, I was ready to give them the whole of the drawings and notations.'

He thereupon conferred with another friend, Sir Benjamin Hawes, and between them they prepared the draft of a letter to Lord Derby, then Prime Minister, in which they were careful to point out that the Government should apply to the President of the Institution of Civil Engineers, asking him whether it was possible to make an estimate of the cost, and, if so, whether a mechanical engineer could be found to construct it and the probable expense.

This plan was communicated by Lord Rosse, but unfortunately once again there was a change of Government and Charles Babbage's hopes were dashed to the ground. 'Science', he said, 'was weighed against gold by a new standard, and it was resolved to proceed no further.' He continued in the way which had now become habitual to him by saying that he received neither an acknowledgement of his labours, nor even the offer of those honours or rewards given to men who devoted themselves to purely scientific investigations. 'I cannot but feel that whilst the public has already derived advantage from my labours, I have myself only experienced loss and neglect', he wrote to Lord Derby on 5th January 1852.

The Prime Minister referred the matter to the Chancellor of the Exchequer. This was Benjamin Disraeli, a redoubtable foe, who roused the best and the worst in Charles Babbage. All that Disraeli knew, apart from what he may have been told by George Airy, the Astronomer-Royal, was that no machine had ever been *finished*. His reply was therefore that the new project would be indefinitely expensive, the ultimate success problematical and the expenditure utterly incapable of being calculated.

This created one of the most contemptuous, but funniest, retorts ever made by Charles Babbage. As to any doubt of its mathematical principles, he said, this was excusable in the Chancellor of the Exchequer who was himself too practically acquainted with the fallibility of his own figures, over which the severe duties of his office had stultified his brilliant imagination. Far other figures were dear to him, those of speech, in which it could not be denied that he was indeed pre-eminent. Any junior clerk in his office might have told him that the power of computing tables by differences merely required a knowledge of simple addition. But the machine upon which everybody could calculate had little chance of fair play from the man on whom nobody could calculate.

The new difference engine 'can not only calculate the millions the ex-chancellor squandered, but it can deal with the smallest quantities, nay it feels even for zeros'. And he added in a footnote: 'It discovers the roots of equations by feeling whether all the figures in a certain column are zeros.' He continued: 'It is as conscious as Lord Derby himself is of the presence of a negative *quantity*, and it is not beyond the ken of either of them to foresee the existence of impossible ones.' In yet another footnote he said: 'It may be necessary to explain to the unmathematical reader and to the ex-Chancellor of the Exchequer that *impossible quantities* in algebra are something like mares' nests in ordinary life.'

Amusing though his remarks were, the misanthropy or persecution complex from which he was now suffering was not improved by this disappointing outcome; and was greatly aggravated about this time by another dispute with Sheepshanks.

The first difference engine had been excluded from the Exhibition of 1851. According to Charles, the name of the author of the *Economy of Manufactures* was thought unworthy by the Government to be placed on the Commission, nor was it thought proper to exhibit the difference engine, although it was the property of the nation, the Commissioners being 'as insensible to the greatest mechanical as to, what has been regarded by some, the greatest intellectual triumph of their country'.

At the same time, prizes, one of £5,000, were offered to exhibitors, and Charles hoped to win one with a model of his invention of occulting lights for lighthouses and night signalling. But before the model was ready the highest prizes were reduced and the others withdrawn. Charles considered this a breach of faith and refused to have anything more to do with the Exhibition.

He published a book entitled *The Exposition of 1851, or Views of the Industry, the Science and the Government of England*, in which he devoted many chapters to practical ways of arranging the exhibition. These are of no interest to posterity, but in Chapter XII he returned to the main theme of *The Decline of Science in England*, entitling it 'Intrigues of Science'. Apart from anything else, he was somewhat equivocal in this, saying, for example, that Professor Moll did not contradict *facts* in his pamphlet, only answered *opinions*; while, according to Sheepshanks, the book was 'chiefly devoted to a relation of the persecutions of which Mr. Babbage imagines himself to have been the object'.

What had happened was this: both in the book and at the meeting of the Board of Visitors to the Greenwich Royal Observatory in 1853, Charles had 'calumniated' Sheepshanks and the latter in 1854 retaliated with a tract of ninety-two pages. In it the author also attacked that inveterate trouble-maker of Campden Hill, Sir James South, who had recently written to the *Mechanics' Magazine* saying that Sheepshanks, in order to avoid paying duty on bringing one of Jecker's circles into England, had had Troughton's name engraved on it. In this South was supported by Charles Babbage. Sheepshanks could not ignore the charge of dishonesty. He had to admit it, but denied the rest of Sir James's story, adding: 'I attribute Mr. Babbage's blundering pertinacity to a diseased mind.'

Sheepshanks' admission of what he had done thirty years before—'I own that I am now heartily ashamed of this transaction'—was not very creditable on the part of one who was at the time a law student and was later to become a clergyman; in spite of this, or because it was natural to the author, the whole of his diatribe was written in the style of 'What a clever fellow am I'; while in his bland assumption of superiority over Charles Babbage and in his references to his friendship with George Airy he was extremely offensive.

Yet in a way Charles Babbage had asked for it. In his own book he linked up Sheepshanks with the Whigs, assigning his own unpopularity with successive governments to political causes. He then changed his tactics, saying that he had traced the connection of Sheepshanks, through his friend the Astronomer Royal, with the Government. According to Airy's own statement he was their adviser on all scientific subjects. The difference and analytical engines were questions of pure science. If the Astronomer Royal had maintained that they were either useless or impracticable then the grounds of their opinion must have been stated and, if published, the solidity of these grounds might be examined. He then added one of his favourite grouses: this was that the highest position to which a man of science could attain was a baronetcy, and the highest salary about £1,000 a year—a position inferior to the Army, Navy, Church and Bar.

Having dealt with Sir James South, Sheepshanks, on the other hand, was in honour bound to turn to Charles, and this he did with gusto, saying that he had for years been to this gentleman 'a very bugbear—one to whom he has ascribed all sorts of injuries and calamities, and persecutions, and with such confidence that I fear some unsuspecting people, ignorant of his malady, may believe him. I have no hope of removing his monomania, nor . . . do I mind what Mr. Babbage may think of me . . . though I never had any doubt of his extraordinary talents in analysis and the science of symbols, I never could make him out to be anything but a very wrong-headed mortal on other subjects. . . .'

He then turned specifically to the charge of influencing the Government. Great expectations had been raised and a large sum of money wasted, he said. And if any idea entered any sane head that some occult agency was at work then Mr. Babbage must have put it there.

Sheepshanks may or may not have been speaking the truth in his next tirade—for it is possible that he knew nothing of what Airy had said to Sir Robert Peel in 1842, namely that the difference engine was worthless. Be this as it may, Sheepshanks asserted that he had never heard that the Government consulted Mr. Airy before he learned it from Mr. Babbage's book; but, he added, if the Government did consult Mr. Airy it acted very wisely, and if the latter gave an opinion Sheepshanks thought it almost certain that it was a judicious one.

'The best authority in this country, except perhaps the Astronomer Royal,' continued Sheepshanks, going right back to 1823 and, at the same time, making a laughing stock of himself to posterity, 'the late Dr. Thomas Young thought the money to be laid out on the calculating machine would be better employed as a fund for calculation. Seeing that we have got *nothing* for our £17,000 but Mr. Babbage's grumbling, I think many people will be of Dr. Thomas Young's opinion, though it earned him the undying hostility of Mr. Babbage.'

The Astronomer Royal would confirm him in his assertion that he had never tried to influence him against the calculating machine, Sheepshanks declared. The only 'confession' he had to make was that soon after the passing of the Reform Bill he was seated at a nobleman's dinner table when a lady asked him, the full length of the table, whether the calculating machine would not be of great service in the computation of the Nautical Almanac.

'My reply', said Sheepshanks, 'was that I did not think it would. . . . My querist was a countess and there were perhaps three or four cabinet ministers present. After this "full confession" I have nothing to add on the subject.'

But he had. 'Those who know how self-opinionated and wrong-headed Mr. Babbage is . . . will have no difficulty in conceiving that his applications to Government must have been considered a *bore* by both ministers and secretaries.'

Saturnine, no doubt, about being called a bore, Charles could not have helped being gratified by the reference to the fidelity and support of the lady fairy. And why he cared at all about Airy and Sheepshanks remains a mystery, for his inventions spoke for themselves to all men of goodwill.

Thus in spite of the disappointments of the 1851 Exhibition, he perfected his model of the occulting light and exhibited it at one of the upper windows at Dorset Street, where, said Henry Babbage, 'it was visible from anywhere down Manchester Street up to the first cross road from his house'. At Brussels in 1853 there was a congress of naval officers from all the maritime nations, and Charles showed it to them. There was only one copy of a paper about it, and when the Russian representative asked to borrow it for a few hours he gladly agreed. The Russian hastily copied it and sent the copy to his own Government. A few years later Charles was told that occulting solar lights were used by the Russians during the siege of Sebastopol.

This, a typical part of sharp practice on the part of the Russians, was regarded by Charles as complimentary, although in the event an English naval officer, later Admiral Colomb, got most of the credit and all the money for the invention, his patent being taken out in 1862. 'The lights are called Morse's lights', said Henry, adding that Morse's notation undoubtedly took less time to operate, though it could not be so easily learned as the simple numerical system.

About the same time, Charles Babbage perfected his invention of the ophthalmoscope for examining the inner structure of the eye. A paper on this was communicated by T. Wharton Jones, F.R.S., to the *British and Foreign Medical Review*, October 1854.

It is tragic that such a benefactor to the human race should have been so concerned with opponents like Airy and Sheepshanks and with material matters that usually belong to men of infinitely lower intellectual calibre. Yet he was concerned with them, and to ignore this concern is not only to ignore part of his character but also, paradoxically enough, to misunderstand the clue to much of his lack of worldly success.

25

Henry at Dorset Street

*

As THE soldiers were going from England to the war in the Crimea, the soldier from India, Henry Babbage, was coming to England on leave. He had served for ten years and was on furlough for three. He was now thirty years old and married, with a child of his own, Georgiana Rachel, born in 1852. On his grandmother's death in 1845 he had inherited a third share of £10,000 under the will of his grandfather, Benjamin Babbage. With this and his pay, he was independent of his father, and was no longer afraid of him.

In spite of his work and his social activities, Charles Babbage, now aged sixty-three, must have been a lonely man, and whether for this reason, or because his former favourite, Herschel, had either settled, or was about to settle, in South Australia, having explored and surveyed part of the north-western area of that colony, he welcomed Henry and his wife, to whom he took an immediate liking, going to the length of creating a comfortable and convenient nursery on the upper floor. One of his minor eccentricities was to place a looking glass on the sideboard in the dining-room so that he could see Minnie Babbage's reflection without looking at her.

Occasionally, but only occasionally, Charles had differences with his son. Once he left the dining-room saying that he would not argue with one who shifted his ground. Once they were discussing a cipher and Henry deluded him, showing his triumph. Charles was very angry and told him that he was a smart fellow, but should be careful not to become too smart. On another occasion he asked: 'Now what was your first serious mistake in life, Henry?' The young man felt that his father had some joke against him, so he retorted instantly: 'Alas, my choice of a parent.' Charles had to laugh at the absurdity, and turned it off by exclaiming: 'What an undutiful son!'

His heart was won, however, by Henry's interest in mechanical pursuits and in his willingness to accompany his father on a round of those soirées and parties still so dear to Charles's heart. Among other achievements, Henry solved a cipher set by a Mr. Thwaites, who hoped to win with it the medal of the Society of Arts. 'I had used the known to reach the unknown and my father was pleased.'

On a visit to Boughton, Henry was filled with childhood memories when Dugald and he were left at the lodge with the Powells. He met Mrs. Powell, who gave the handsome stranger 'a warm embrace'.

The following winter, 1855, was very severe; there was much snow in London and by the middle of February the River Thames was nearly covered by ice. Colonel Phipps, Prince Albert's equerry, asked whether he could show the Prince a model of the occulting telegraph. Soon afterwards Minnie Babbage gave birth to a son, and, said her husband: 'My father and I were at dinner when the nurse, Jane, came running down to tell us.' A few days later he accompanied his father to Somerset House and saw Scheutz's machine, and began to make the mechanical notation.

This machine was made by a Swedish printer after reading Dr. Lardner's article on the difference engine in the *Edinburgh Review* in 1834. It was a small machine, consisting of four differences and fourteen places of figures, and was capable of printing tables. In principle it was quite different from Charles Babbage's machine, and, although aided by a few grants and the Swedish Academy, the inventor succeeded only after great difficulties and ruinous expenditure. To everyone's surprise, Charles Babbage did everything he could to foster its success and was, undoubtedly, instrumental in its being awarded the French Gold Medal, greatly to the gratitude and pleasure of the inventor. It was eventually bought for Dudley Observatory at Albany, U.S.A., by John F. Rathbone, a citizen of that town, while an exact copy was made by Donkin & Co. for the British Government and used in the Registrar-General's Department at Somerset House.

There were several reasons why Charles should be so amiable: his own machine had inspired it; it was infinitely less ambitious than his own, and its completion therefore much easier; its mere existence proved that a calculating machine of this kind could not only be *made* but would also *work*.

Some years later Charles Babbage wrote to his friend Miss (afterwards Baroness) Burdett Coutts, who, when Lord Elgin was appointed Governor General of India, told Charles that if he would not speak to Lord Elgin about Henry she would. Charles, who believed in merit and not patronage, said—after reluctantly giving Henry's address in India:

'I had no interest whatever to get him promotion. He obtained that office entirely by a steady attention to his previous duties, which acquired for him the friendship as well as the approbation of his immediate superiors.

'Some few years since he came home on furlough and during his residence with me gave some portion of his attention to mechanical subjects. During this visit the Swedish Difference Engine for Calculating and Printing Mathematical Tables arrived in London. My son studied and, applying to it a system of signs which is called Mechanical Notation, he made himself master of the subject. He then explained it, in two papers, one read at the meeting of the British Association at Glasgow, the other before the Institution of Civil Engineers in London.

'I took these illustrations of the Swedish Engine with me to the Great International Exhibition of 1855 at Paris, and I have good reason to believe that they contributed largely to convince the jury that the inventor, M. Scheutz, was worthy of the highest reward they could bestow—namely, their Gold Medal.'

Henry, in his father's eyes, had made good, and when in November 1856 his furlough ended, the parting was very different from the first: Charles saw the family off at Waterloo, and watched the train until it was out of sight. 'It must have been a wretched day for him, for we had certainly helped to enliven his life and entered into all his pursuits', said Henry.

Charles Babbage must indeed have had some unhappy memories at this time, reflecting on the two Georgianas, and four of his sons, his parents and Lady Lovelace—all now dead. Perhaps some memories were more nostalgic than unhappy. There was the note recently received from Lord Ockham at Millwall, where he may have docked from a merchantman. He was now twenty, and said that he was happy to accept Charles's invitation and would be at Dorset Street at 4 p.m.

There was a note of 28th April 1851, in which Dickens told him that as a steward to a farewell dinner on William Macready's retirement the expenses were well over receipts and Charles's share was £3 10s. Would he please pay it into Dickens's accounts at Coutts Bank? There was a much earlier letter from Dickens in 1844, one of the funniest which he ever wrote:

'I regret to say we are placed in the preposterous situation of being obliged to postpone our little dinner party on Saturday, by reason of having no house to dine in. We have not been burnt out, but a desirable widow (as a tenant, I mean) proposed only last Saturday to take our own house for the whole term of our intended absence abroad, on condition that she had possession of it to-day.

'We fled & were driven into this place, which has no convenience for the production of any other banquet than a cold collation of plate & linen—the only comfort we have not left behind us.

'My consolation lies in knowing what sort of dinner you would have had, if you had come here, & in looking forward to claiming the fulfilment of your kind promise when we are again at home.'

In 1851 Charles Babbage's old friend, the Duke of Somerset, a Fellow of the Royal Society, died, and many affectionate invitations to dinner followed from his widow, imploring him to wear morning dress and to wrap up warmly. In one she asked him to come at 10 p.m. to meet the Persian Ambassador, who was anxious to meet 'the greatest man of his day'.

And much, much longer ago, in 1838 or 1839, Charles Darwin had refused invitations to the parties at Dorset Street because 'I would be sure to meet people to whom I had sworn that I never went out'.

And even longer ago than this, in 1833, when riding one of his favourite hobby horses, Charles Babbage had published a pamphlet, *Observations on Peerage for Life*. He still believed that all peerages should be conferred for life only, the heirs apparent to have and to use the second title, without a seat in the House of Lords; and peers created for life should take precedence over hereditary peers of the same rank. This pamphlet was reprinted in 1856. It evoked a letter from a friend, signed: 'Ever sincerely yours, R. Hastings'. It was clearly from a lady who seems to have had an unfortunate experience. It may have been Lady Hastings.

'I object radically to a hereditary peerage, for I am sure we have enough imbecile aristocrats who certainly do not deserve their name. I would give peerages as rewards for great deeds, whether intellectual or physical, but certainly not to monied, commercial and other individuals who have done nothing to merit distinction; and as clever parents do not unfortunately beget clever children as a rule, there the distinction should end, instead of being perpetuated by a race of keepers, grooms, or perhaps something not even so intellectual as that.'

This, even at his gloomiest, must have afforded Charles a smile.

As, indeed, must recollections of his ballet.

One night at the German opera, after observing the different tints in a scene by moonlight, he suddenly thought of coloured lighting for the stage. As a result, he who disliked music and had never cared much for the theatre, suddenly became a choreographer. He devised the 'rainbow' dance, into which at times 'sixty damsels in pure white' would assume all the prismatic colours and, at others, resemble a shooting star. From this arose his ballet *Alethes and Iris*, the moral of which was to look into all the works of creation.

Because of the danger of fire, it came to nothing, unfortunately, the manager saying that if the house were burnt his customers would be burnt, too. Charles agreed that it was a valid objection, 'for though he could have insured the building he could not have insured his audience'.

26

The Unphilosophical Philosopher

*

As THE years passed, time went much more quickly, and Charles Babbage, who in 1862 was seventy-one, agreed that the finished part of the first difference engine should be shown at the exhibition of that year at South Kensington, London. This was due largely to the influence of his friend William Gravatt, the engineer, who had had much to do with the Scheutz machine. And, although he considered the surroundings unsatisfactory, Charles was gratified that it should be shown at all. According to him, in spite of pressing requests, it was due entirely to the British Government that it had been exhibited neither in London in 1851, nor in New York nor in France; while Russian universities were unable to take back accounts of the mechanical notation.

The difference engine was eventually shown in 'a small hole, 4 feet 4 inches in front by 5 feet deep', being hemmed in by other exhibits. There was very little light, and the machine could be seen by no more than six people at a time.

His friend and biographer Wilmot Buxton, of the Chancery Bar, who possessed a profound knowledge of the mathematical principles, also took part. He said that Charles Babbage frequently visited the exhibition to explain the mysteries of the engine to 'a crowd of anxious and curious observers'. Charles tried to avoid this, but it was not easy because for one thing there was a widespread misapprehension, even among educated people, that the difference engine had been the means of discovering certain mysterious laws of numbers which, without its aid, could not have been accomplished. Charles tried, with little success, to dispel this, and he decided to write a popular pamphlet, but, as the exhibition closed before he could finish it, he incorporated it in his so-called autobiography *Passages from the Life of a Philosopher*, which was started in the autumn of 1862.

Even in the first stages he was admonished by the correspondent who signed herself in the Continental fashion, 'Countess Teleki'. Their mutual friend was General Menabrea, who was to become Prime Minister of United Italy in 1867. The first of the Countess's letters was written from Turin on 26th November 1863.

'. . . I have seen Menabrea, who made very great enquiries after you and the Anal: [engine] for the completion of which he is extremely anxious, and hopes that you will not let the continual contriving of fresh improvements stand in the way of really constructing the engine itself, to which I can only add an entreaty that you will not forget the wise old French proverb which says *le mieux est l'ennemie du bien*.

'I told Menabrea too of the book, which is to see the light of day some day. For the sake of all the poor hungry souls who love fun, and have been starving ever since the days of Sidney Smith, do leave all the stories and hard cuts not yet written for the second edition, and let us have the first to feed upon at once; but not a word did I hint as to the intended dedication, either to his King or himself. I thought these had better come as a surprise when you send him the books. . . .'

In reply Charles Babbage evidently tried to allay their misgivings about the analytical engine, for the Countess wrote again on 10th December 1863, still from Turin.

'I am delighted to hear that you are satisfied at last with the mechanism of the new carriage, and that you will not seek a better, for with your ingenuity I am always afraid of some fresh idea striking you as likely to be an improvement, and of your setting to work in consequence on another set of drawings, instead of constructing the engine itself, but this time I do hope you will be satisfied, since the carriage, which is the soul of the whole, is ready to do its work with all desirable speed and simplicity. . . .

'I shall hope to find a great deal done for me to see and hear about when I return to England, and since you talk about the book being out in February, I shall hope to read that while I am still in Italy, and to enjoy the merited castigations you bestow on so many humbugs. . . .

'Your friend Menabrea is a desperately busy man, with his harbours and his railways, the responsibility for all of which is in his hands, still he comes to see me tolerably often of an evening, and sometimes we meet at the Chamber of Deputies, where I am rather in the habit of frequenting the Diplomatic Tribune whenever there is a stormy and exciting debate.'

About this time Charles received proofs of the book, and took a perverse pleasure in reading and correcting them, for it was not strictly an autobiography at all but a volume of memoirs, consisting of amusing anecdotes and after-dinner stories, as well as a sarcastic recital of his dealings with successive Governments and statesmen. He made no reference whatever to his wife or his married life; apart from mentioning her briefly as translator and annotator of Menabrea's paper he ignored Lady Lovelace. Much of it was extremely witty, hence the description of him as a 'humorist manqué'. But sometimes he tried to be too funny, as, for example, on the title page:

Below his name, among his degrees and decorations (he had a few, mainly foreign), he printed in large type: 'Commander of the Italian Order of St. Maurice and St. Lazarus.' And, lower down, two lines from Don Juan:

> 'I'm a philosopher. Confound them all—
> Birds, beasts and men; but no, not womankind.'

Lower still, he printed the following piece of nonsense that was somehow undignified in the circumstances:

'I now gave my mind to philosophy; the great object of my ambition was to make out a complete system of the universe, including and comprehending the origin, causes, consequences and termination of all things. Instead of countenance, encouragement and applause, which I should have received from everyone who has the true dignity of an oyster at heart, I was exposed to calumny and misrepresentation. While engaged in my great work on the universe, some even went so far as to accuse me of infidelity, such is the malignity of oysters.— "Autobiography of an Oyster", deciphered by the aid of photography in the shell of a philosopher of that race—recently scalloped.'

The dedication ignored General Menabrea, and was made to 'The Sovereign of United Italy, the country of Archimedes and of Galileo': Victor Emmanuel II was the son of Charles Albert, who had been kind to Charles Babbage in 1840, and to whom the latter was indebted 'for the first public and official acknowledgment' of the analytical engine.

Something totally different, however, angered John Murray, the publisher, who wrote from 50 Albemarle Street:

'When you did me the honor first to consult me about your book you recited to me a certain epigram and asked me what I thought of it.

'I told you I thought it grossly offensive, and that the publication of it would greatly damage you and your book. I had hoped to have heard or seen nothing more of it, but in cutting up the leaves of Sig. 2 B (which had not been submitted to me in proof) since you left me this morning I regret to find this offensive epigram is printed at page 370.

'I do not expect and will not condescend to ask an author to alter any passage of his book to please me. I have therefore no alternative but to decline proceeding with the publication of the book, which I am glad has not proceeded so far as to prevent your making other arrangements.

'I lose no time in writing to you what I would have told you to your face, had I been aware when you called that the epigram was included in the work.'

This was the offending passage:

'The clever and eccentric member for East Surrey, the late Henry Drummond, who founded a professorship of Political Economy at Oxford, made in the House of Commons a most amusing, though rather strong, speech against the modern miracles of the Roman Catholic church, in which he spoke of "their bleeding pictures, their winking statues, and the Virgin's milk". On this some profane wag wrote the following couplet:

"Sagacious Drummond, explain with your divinity:
Why reject the milk, yet swallow the virginity?"

'Probably some clever fellow of that faith was at the bottom
of this mischief; for I have observed that the cleverest fellows
seem to think that the merit of adhering to a cause entitles
them to the right of quizzing it.

'I was particularly struck with this idea when I saw, for the
first time, at Cologne, the celebrated picture of St. Ursula
and her eleven thousand virgins. The artist has quietly made
every one of them more or less matronly.'

Characteristically, Charles refused to remove the offending
passage, and found another publisher, Longmans Green, under
whose imprint the book appeared.

He had sent proofs to the Countess Harley-Teleki, and she
wrote, returning them, from Bologna on the 19th January 1864.
She, too, was not amused, although she began by saying that
the scenes were very funny and hit hard, as could not fail
to be the case, for whenever he took to quizzing, it could not be
questioned that he did it thoroughly, not sparing the lash,
like small diplomatic powers when something was done which
they did not like, but were not strong enough to resist. She
continued:

'I must enter a protest against the publication. I laughed
but it was against my conscience, for seriously I do not at all
admire your making such unmerciful attacks on yourself
in print. If it were a spoken impromptu, it would be a good
jeu d'esprit, but I think there is a Latin adage to the effect that
what is written remains, and for your friends' sakes, if not for
your own, you should not caricature yourself for the amusement
of those who know no better than to believe you, (in the simple
faith that what is printed *must* be true). . . .

'I utterly and absolutely protest against the spirit of mischief
which had taken possession of you when you wrote these
scenes, being allowed its own way, and I am persuaded that if
you consult your friend Mr. Buxton he will agree with me,

that this chapter will do no good service to the Analytical [engine]. It is very good fun for those who know you, but to the public you should not pretend to treat science so lightly, and as your title page asserts the book to be the work of a philosopher, I am not quite sure (stronger reasons apart) that [it] is perfectly consistent to shew you remember the misdeeds of Lords A and Flumm so well.

'I wish I could hear of something more being done to the Analytical than drawings only. My longing is to see it at work, with all its wheels and its carriages busy calculating. With all my belief in its powers, it would still be more satisfactory to see it really at work. For its sake also I shall be very glad when the book is out, and fairly off your hands, that there may be no other work to take up your time.

'I am very glad to hear that you have been successfully relieved from the inconvenience you were suffering in your back, and that there need be no apprehension of its occurrence. . . .

'My respectful salutations to both your parrots, if they are not too jealous to accept them. . . .'

But he would never finish the machine, as the Countess must, in her heart of hearts, have known. He was obsessed by the drawings. As soon as he had finished one set he thought of an improvement, and started on another set, and so on and so on, *ad infinitum*. He could not rid himself of what had become a disease, and say 'Enough'.

He was nevertheless very convincing. He sent copies to Napoleon III and the Empress Eugénie, saying that the analytical engine was so much simplified that it should soon be finished, and he was considering what should be its first essay.

'The vast calculations made in France during one of the most painful periods of her history naturally claim my attention . . . The first task therefore which I shall propose . . . will be to recalculate the whole of the table of natural sines to every 10,000th. part of the quadrant. This however will be but a trifling exertion of its powers. In the earliest period of its existence it ought to be employed in re-computing the formulae and in verifying the coefficients of Laplace in his investigations of the three bodies.

'After that it might be used to develope the still more complicated problem of the three bodies when they are acting under the conditions that each is a magnet with several poles and that the transmission of magnetism, unlike that of gravity, is not instantaneous.'

In spite of his critics, the book was well received by the Press and public, for it contained among other things many ingenious and entertaining examples of puzzles, anagrams and the squaring of words.

He described his cipher dictionary, or, to be more precise, dictionaries, the object of which was to make a complete analysis of the language—in this case English—in which the cipher was written. He had had a good dictionary copied into twenty-four others, one comprising words of one letter, another of two letters and so on up to twenty-six. These were classified into yet others, and the latter again classified and so on, until the whole contained half a million words.

There was an amusing reference to Vidocq, the French detective, who could reduce his height at will by one and a half inches. Charles was fascinated by this, and demanded a medical explanation, but there was none. Vidocq found the gift a most excellent disguise.

Picking locks was another of Charles Babbage's favourite pursuits, and one on which he was an expert, for it concerned one of his own subjects—combinations. In his book he related some very interesting anecdotes on the subject.

The main critics were among his own friends and associates, though one of them, Sir James Paget, the surgeon, told him that it was 'the most remarkable combination of fun, philosophy and sarcasm that I have ever read', and another, Herbert Spencer, said: 'So long as our statesmen are educated as they are, I suppose we must expect them to be incapable of understanding the importance of science.'

On the 6th September 1864, however, Dr. John Davy, F.R.S., wrote to him from Lesketh House, Ambleside, about the attack on his brother, Sir Humphry, in which Charles Babbage accused the latter of a wilful breach of faith in the matter of the junior secretaryship, and of improperly appropriating money belonging to the Royal Society. Dr. Davy added: 'All I now recollect pertaining to what may be comprised in this—that he held in estimation your exhibitions [?] and did all in his power to aid in procuring you funds for the construction of your calculating engine.'

Although he gave Davy the credit for the moderation of his tone, Charles drafted a very churlish reply. After due consideration, he said that he could neither add by way of explanation, nor retract. All could be verified by consulting the Council book, and elsewhere.

Sir James South then entered the arena attacking his old friend Charles Babbage on 20th September 1864, Charles, eventually discovering that it was the other who had encouraged Davy to write in the first place. He then dragged in the peace-loving John Herschel, and the whole was published in *The Philosophical Magazine*. It was an unseemly and unedifying brawl.

Of far more interest, because it threw important light on the mind of Charles Babbage, was the matter ventilated by Professor Lyon Playfair, later Lord Playfair, of Edinburgh University. He wrote on 1st December 1864:

'I have been reading with great interest *Recollections of a Philosopher*, and wish to correct one statement in it—that the name of the author of *The Economy of Manufactures* never occurred to any of the promoters of the Exhibition of 1851.

'I was not connected in any way with the origin of that Exhibition . . . But when it was in difficulty . . . Sir Robert Peel asked me as a personal favor to himself to take an active part in it and introduced me to the Prince Consort, by whom I was authorized to make any proposal . . .

'I proposed that there should be responsible industrial commissioners who should take the scientific working of the Exhibition and aid the business executives with their advice and knowledge . . .

'I further suggested that you should be made the Chief

Industrial Commissioner and that I and no doubt others would be proud and happy to act under you in that undertaking.

'I found at my next interview with the Prince Consort that he was pleased with the suggestion, but as regarded the general idea and the proposal of your name, stating at the same time that he had intended to have made me Chief Commissioner, but that if you undertook the office you of course would be head.

'I was then authorized to see whether the proposal would be entertained in other quarters. I have no recollection of Sir Robert Peel's opinion in the matter, but I know generally that I found it impossible to carry out that proposal. You were supposed to be so utterly hostile to Government not then Sir R. Peel's, and so dissatisfied with it, that I was not permitted to sound you.

'The question was soon settled by a man whose name I had never heard of being nominated to act with me, and the "Industrial Commission" necessarily sank in importance and use. I had received so much kindness and personal friendship from Sir R. Peel that I could not refuse his urgent request to go on with the work though I felt much inclined to relinquish it when you were not asked at least to help in the undertaking.

'It is now a matter of history and I thought that you would like to know that you had *not* been forgotten by all.'

Charles Babbage made three drafts of his reply to Playfair. The first two were ungracious, and the third, dated 12th December 1864, was better.

He apologized for the delay in replying to the other's letter, which was not less honourable to himself than 'an act of justice to the late lamented Prince Consort'.

The reason why he was occluded from the Exhibition, said Charles, he never enquired into, much less was he interested or disposed to seek after the agents by whom his occlusion had been effected. Of course, he continued, equivocally, or perhaps forgetfully, it was inevitable that the public should speculate upon a circumstance which seemed so directly to be aimed at himself, and no doubt many in the absence of any accurate evidence might—and he had reason to believe did—

attribute his occlusion to the late Prince Consort and his advisers. However, Charles trusted that he had always done justice to the Prince's character and memory by carefully abstaining from drawing any hasty conclusions or indulging in any way an hypothesis in the matter, and although the circumstances might have favoured suspicions of an unfriendly influence, he never believed the Prince capable of using his high influence in any way unbecoming his illustrious position, and until Charles read Playfair's letter he was utterly without the means of forming any rational conjecture upon the subject.

He continued in the same equivocal strain:

'I must however admit that I am greatly surprised at the revelation of the real cause of my occlusion. You write "You were supposed to be so utterly hostile to Government not then Sir R. Peel's and so dissatisfied with it that I was not permitted to sound you." Now, certainly, amongst the vague conjectures which have from time to time floated in my mind, nothing so extravagant as the possibility of being occluded by any political considerations ever haunted my imagination. I have never at any period of a somewhat lengthened public career forced my political opinions into prominent notice; such as they are, I claim the right of having them judged by my printed works, for which I am quite willing to be responsible; and I have no reason to regret any political opinion I have ever ventured to ventilate. Even during the distracted period which immediately followed the passing of the Reform Bill, in which I actively participated, I expressed opinions in my address to the Finsbury electors which I can still contemplate with satisfaction, and in which—though they were elicited under circumstances of unusual political excitement—I now see little which I should be disposed to modify; supposing the political circumstances of that disturbed period to exist at the present time.

'I deem it especially a subject of [con] gratulation that I have never been misled or hurried into the formation of suspicious injuries to the memory of the illustrious personage whose loss we all lament and that the most pleasing impressions of his character have never been obliterated. I have seen and admired him under circumstances in which the highest characteristics of his intellectual character commanded my admiration—those who knew him best would doubtless be his warmest admirers. I who unfortunately enjoyed but a very limited opportunity of judging his intellectual powers always thought that he possessed elements of mental capacity but little likely to be understood or appreciated by the persons with whom his exalted rank necessarily brought him into contact.'

He concluded by asking permission to publicize the important contents of the letter in a future edition of his book.

Lyon Playfair gave permission on the 20th February 1865, but added this warning:

'In your former letter there was one misapprehension of my meaning. The objection urged to your employment was not on political grounds but because you were considered dissatisfied with the action of Govt. in regard to your engine and would not likely allow those feelings of dissatisfaction to subside. You will recollect that although the Royal Commission of the Exhibition was independent of the Govt. that it was chiefly composed of men with whom you had been in correspondence on the subject of your engine and that actual co-operation with the existing Govt. was necessarily constant.

'I am most anxious that there should be no misunderstanding on this point, as I have always admired the absence of political consideration in successive Govts. in the employment of men of science. I have personally been employed by every Govt. since 1844 and have never once been asked my political opinion.'

This may well be the truth about a very controversial matter; and in any case it completely cut the ground from under Charles's feet; but such was the state of his mind that he seems not to have seen it in that light, for writing later in the year to Gravatt he said that he had often been asked by men in high position to explain the real causes which had impeded the progress of the difference engine. One of them had been explained by Lyon Playfair in a letter which he had been advised to publish. Not to do so would be doing an injustice to the late Prince Consort. And he then reverted to another familiar grouse, citing Robert Stephenson, the engineer, as yet one more victim of the Astronomer Royal.

27

'My Dear Duchess'

*

ONE of the more cheerful results of *Passages from the Life of a Philosopher* was the number of Americans who wrote to Charles Babbage. He had always liked Americans and they liked him. He had been asked to invite Catherine Sedgwick, the novelist, to one of his earliest parties in 1829. At another, while most of the guests crowded round the Silver Lady, an American was explaining the difference engine to a Dutch professor. As Charles gazed from room to room, another guest asked him: 'What new mischief are you meditating?' Charles immediately retorted: 'Look, in that further room—England! Look again at this—two foreigners!'

This liking for Americans had been furthered in 1854 by their adoption of the occulting telegraph. Henry Reed, Professor of English Literature at Philadelphia, who was concerned in this, wrote to him on 18th September 1854, from Rydal Mount, where he was staying with Wordsworth, pressing him for the last time to return with him. Charles, however, still felt it would be useless unless he could stay twelve months, which was not possible, and he thus had a lucky escape. Two days later Reed sailed with his sister and Charles wrote on the letter that the *Arctic* steamer was lost and both perished.

In 1868 he sent Henry W. Longfellow a copy of his book, and the poet replied from Bonchurch regretting that he had to leave London without seeing him, but ending 'with kind regards'.

In view of his 'world-wide reputation' a United States Government despatch agent asked for his advice in purchasing the best calculating machine, to which Charles replied that his machines were not the kind required, and were not, in any case, for sale.

He received a letter from Washington D.C. in May 1869. It was from a Captain H. W. Howgate, of the U.S. Army, who said that after some years an old form of cipher had been finally settled upon. It was easily worked and read with the key, 'but without the key has thus far defied the experts on this side of the Atlantic'. From a casual remark in the book, however, the writer suspected that Charles had the key, and wondered whether he would write and confirm this.

A few months before his death Charles received from an American named Daniel Vaughan a note about the latter's paper, *The Effect of Tides on Planetary Motion*. The author was somewhat doubtful about the originality of some of his own researches and conclusions.

These letters gave him great pleasure, especially at this time, when his long life was coming to a close. Thus he was ill in August 1863, the Duchess of Somerset making her usual kind enquiries, likewise his sister Mrs. Hollier, and her son Tom, rector of Preston, near Bath, who begged his uncle to stay with him in order to recuperate. And Lord Glenelg, writing from Rome in January 1864, asked whether the operation then pending had been tried.

In September 1865 the Countess Harley-Teleki asked him to stay with her at Eynwood, and he replied quite unselfconsciously:

'Many thanks for your kind invitation. This hot weather has almost knocked me up.

'I have been working at the most difficult part of the analytical engine, the half zero carriage. It has been the greatest and most continuous effort I have ever encountered and I feel the effect upon my health, and also that I am not equal to any repetition of such exertions.'

He put off the visit until later, when, she said, they could have 'much philosophic conversation', which she would try accurately to transmit to their friend Menabrea. And, although he recovered for a time, his sister tried continuously to keep up his spirits, saying in October 1867 that a visitor was at Preston Rectory, a grey parrot, who was 'the most amusing guest and talks quite plainly and almost incessantly'.

One of the most tiresome things to which Charles Babbage was subjected in his last years was the persecution from some of the subjects of that King to whom he had dedicated his book— the Italian organ-grinders. He was not the only sufferer. There were others, including Thomas Carlyle, John Leech and Mr. Bass, M.P. for Derbyshire, who intended to get up a petition in the House of Commons. Modern readers who suffer from the noise of jet engines, electric drills, transistor radio sets and similar nuisances, will sympathize.

As long ago as 1860 he described a typical incident. Having asked a man outside the house to stop and go away, the latter obeyed for a moment and then started again. Charles chased him for about a mile before finding a constable who took the man in charge. But Charles was already becoming notorious, and some of his neighbours encouraged these men, often when he was engaged in difficult calculations. He frequently received threatening and anonymous letters. The mob would often follow him, using epithets and shouting: 'Turn it [the cab] over.' He was accustomed to hearing his name execrated in all parts of London, and having his windows broken. Once a bolt of iron was flung at one of his library windows.

He was driven on one occasion to ask Dr Hooker, then President of the British Association, to ventilate his grievances at a B.A. Meeting, remarking that the previous Friday he and his manservant had gone out to find a constable. None was in sight when wanted. They separated, and Charles was followed through several streets, insulted and shouted at by hundreds of vagabonds, and pelted with mud. Finding a cab, he entered and was driven to a police station, but he received no assistance, and no one was taken into custody. He remarked that this kind of thing had 'destroyed many years of my intellectual working power'.

A charming offer of help came from a woman, Mrs. Ambrose Moore, who wrote from Hastings on 4th March to say that she had met at the British Museum a lady whose husband, the

Count di Tergolina, had much influence over many of the poor Italians in London. If Charles's annoyance rose principally from the Italians, she said, 'many of whom are worthy men, and of a gentle nature, he could probably induce them to abstain from playing near your house'. She believed that the Count would be quite pleased to help in this matter, 'of so little trouble to him, though of so great importance to you'.

In thanking her, he replied that much of his time was occupied in giving instructions for drawings. He had on some occasions paid a guinea a day to his chief assistant and from these interruptions had often had half his time and expense wasted.

Old age, meanwhile, was underlined by the death of one old friend after another. On 6th November 1867 he wrote to condole with the Countess of Rosse, saying: 'I have lost the only friend capable from his knowledge and appreciation of the work of my life and from his position and his great practical experience in mechanism of influencing the faith of my countrymen in it.' Worse was to follow in May 1871 when he wrote to Lady Herschel sympathizing with her feelings 'on the loss of one of the earliest and most valued friends of my life'. His own health, he added, confined him almost to the house, and for this reason he could not pay his last respects. He added a pathetic little note to the copy: 'Draft of letter to Lady Herschel on the death of my friend.'

In the same year he wrote what appears to be his last note. It was in reply to an invitation to dinner from his warm-hearted old friend the Dowager Duchess of Somerset.

My dear Duchess,

Many thanks for your kind invitation to meet Lord Dalhousie, which I would have accepted with much pleasure. The state of my health however prevents me at present from accepting any invitations.

With many thanks and much regret,

I am, my dear Duchess,

Very sincerely Yours,

Charles Babbage

He was becoming very infirm and depressed and, when Henry Babbage, who had distinguished himself in the Indian Mutiny in 1857, arrived with his wife from India in March 1871, Charles was incapable of managing his own affairs, and Henry had to see his uncle, Sir Edward Ryan, about them.

On 5th October, Henry, who was then living at Bromley, received a telegram from Robert Wight, one of his father's workmen, saying that his master was very ill. When Henry arrived he found his father in bed and in great pain, but Charles recognized his son and asked after Minnie. Throughout this last illness he was attended by his friend Sir James Paget, who refused a fee. When the latter suggested a trained nurse, Henry procured one, much to the annoyance of Mr. and Mrs. Collis, the butler and cook, who were so intransigent that Henry had to give them a month's notice. And, although he wrote to the Commissioner of Police, the annoyance from organ-grinders persisted to the end.

Charles was delirious or unconscious for much of the time, but in a lucid period Sir Edward Ryan talked to him about his affairs and urged him to make a new will. This he did. It was copied by Wight, signed by Charles on 13th October 1871, and witnessed by Wight, Eliza Lloyd, the nurse, and Sir James Paget. It was quite simple, leaving everything equally to his three sons, except everything connected with the calculating machine, which was left to Henry, £1,000 to Herschel and £3 monthly to Mary Wilson. It was proved on 13th November, his effects being under £40,000, but leaseholds were also mentioned.

On 14th October Charles was much weaker, suffering from excessive pain. 'It's a long time coming,' he said, referring to death. Once, when Paget asked him what he had eaten, he said he did not know, adding: 'Happy is he who does not remember what he has eaten.' At another time he said: 'Now I am going, as they call it, to the other world: ask me any question you like as to my feelings or thoughts, and I will tell you.' He was not troubled, however; and he seemed to have forgotten the passion of his youth about returning to tell his friends the secrets of that other world.

As the end drew near, he was in a high fever, and tortured by pain and restlessness, and his thoughts were on Georgiana, dead these forty years, for once, looking up at Henry, he said: 'You are like your mother.' And when Henry and Minnie were standing on either side of his bed he murmured: 'What a tableau.'

There were many spasmodic enquiries from friends, but the Dowager Duchess of Somerset was, as always, 'unremitting in her solicitude and kindness, sending him all sorts of good things daily'.

Soon after eleven o'clock on the night of 18th October 1871 Charles murmured: 'What o'clock is it, Henry?' He was told, and thirty-five minutes past the hour he was dead.

He was buried in a brick grave in Kensal Green Cemetery on 24th October within two months of his eightieth birthday. Apart from his three or four immediate connections, there was only 'one solitary mourner', himself, said Wilmot Buxton protesting in a letter to *The Morning Post* that 'a great man' had gone almost unnoticed to the grave. Where were the equipages of the many great men—noble, scientific and literary—who had thronged his famous parties? he enquired.

And well he might protest, for apart from that of Charles Babbage's faithful friend, the Dowager Duchess of Somerset, there was none.

Epilogue

THE BRAIN

*C*HARLES BABBAGE's great calculating machine was his own brain. In an attempt to explain it, Sir Victor Horsley, the surgeon, afterwards examined it but found nothing of significance to the layman. It is still preserved by the Royal College of Surgeons of England.

Dead, to the layman, the brain is an inert mass. Alive, it cannot for obvious reasons be dissected and examined. Ironically, in view of the electronic 'brain', biologists and electronic engineers are co-operating in an attempt to find out, by means of electronic techniques, something of the mysteries of the human brain. To what extent they will succeed remains to be seen, especially regarding that very extraordinary mystery of what constitutes the brain of a man of genius.

One thing about Charles Babbage, however, is certain. In addition to great knowledge and learning, he shared with many notable men a superhuman and dynamic energy, which was physical as well as mental. But even this is not necessarily concomitant with genius. It was his questing brain that distinguished him from all others. This brain was never at rest.

He would sit or walk for hours in his garden at 1 Dorset Street, which he had planted with giant hellebore, examining and speculating on the wonders of nature. A gaudy butterfly, emerging from the chrysalis, he would describe as a marvel, adding that the whole of nature was a standing miracle, showing the true reflection of its Almighty Creator. Even history, which he despised, with its 'unfaithful' record of the 'conflict of follies inspired by the passions of interested men', he believed to be the result of some mysteriously operated great and transcendental laws.

These laws were based on reason and logic. But there are other qualities and emotions: insight, imagination, prevision, love, sexual love (as distinct from lust), kindness and affection, to name some. Charles Babbage himself possessed not a few of these qualities, giving at no time the impression of being all head and no heart. And logic, as Lady Lovelace found to her cost, and as he must have known, was not sufficient, even in racing. Perhaps in his own mind he lumped them together under the general heading 'history', as 'inspired by the passions of interested men', caused by 'some mysteriously operated great and transcendental laws'. Be this as it may, it is odd that one who described himself as a philosopher and aspired to know the origin, causes, consequences and termination of all things, should have ignored human personality and with it, the whole man.

Some peculiar things happened to Charles Babbage's brain at times. It seems first to have become overwrought in 1827 by the conjunction of two things: his failure to finish the difference engine in the time envisaged, and the death of his wife, his father and two of his children. And it was, on some subjects, obsessed. But it never lost the power over his hands. When he was nearly seventy he spent some time at Hartwell Observatory, displaying all his old agility and aptitude in manipulating the instruments.

Although he said in his old age that he hated life but did not want to die, he contradicted himself by remarking that he would gladly give up the remainder of his life if he could be allowed to live three days 500 years hence, assisted by a scientific cicerone who could explain to him the discoveries made since his death. Since the emergence of two world wars could not be predicted in his lifetime, he needed very much less than 500 years. Had he come back within seventy years, in 1936, he would have found another Englishman of genius, Alan Turing, wresting the torch from him and passing it on to others.

But if he had waited yet a further thirty years, and come back today, a century later, he would have found himself acclaimed as the genius he knew himself to be, for electronic devices, used on his own theoretical principles, had transformed his slow-moving brain child into something more practicable, responding almost instantaneously to the commands it was given.

His brain would have been excited to find both worlds, the

Western and the Communist, agog about projected landings
on the moon. Lunar maps, after all, bore his own name, with
those of Herschel II, Robinson and South. They had been
named by Dr. Lee of Hartwell in 1862. A marvel or a miracle
he would have thought the rocket, likewise all kinds of flight,
radio and television, not to mention Captain Cousteau's
attempt to establish man's continuous occupation of the ocean
bed in his 'diving saucer'.

But the actual uses might not have pleased him so much,
the space race as a military undertaking, for example, or the
vulgarity and triviality of so much on television. There was,
too, psycho-analysis, and the interpretation which Freud would
have placed on his own dreams; for waking or sleeping his
brain was always at work. He might, in fact, have had some
unpleasant shocks, as well as pleasant surprises.

These dreams and nightmares were of frequent occurrence.
When a dream became alarming he said to himself: 'This is
only a dream. I should like to see the end of it. I will let it go on
unless it should become very alarming, and then I will awake
out of it.' At other times he would say: 'This is no dream—it
is too real—it is too terrible.' In such cases he awoke in great
distress, either making or imagining that he was making some
great bodily effort.

Again, he often imagined that he was flying through the
air. Sometimes he flew over a deep valley from the top of one
hill to that of another. Occasionally, he was afraid that he
might not have the strength to reach the desired goal, but he
always seemed able to do so. On these occasions it appeared
that he used his arms as wings, on others that he used both arms
and feet as in swimming.

He was much more familiar with another variation of this
dream of flying through the air. This consisted of a uniform
passage without any physical effort. There seemed to be a
power capable of counteracting gravity, he said, so that his
body rose at will above the ground to any required height. He
thus in his dreams rose from the ground and passed along many
streets, sometimes 'on a level with the drawing-room windows
and sometimes with those of the attics'. He also dreamed that

in the same way he passed over large forests just above the topmost branches, raising or lowering himself at will.

'It is remarkable that . . . I have rarely had any sense of bodily effort or even of any motion of my limbs: yet on the other hand I have always had an intense sense of volition.'

It seemed, in fact, that he had the power of flying only through the intense exertion of his will to do so; as a result of which he almost always awoke with a sense of great fatigue, often with a severe headache, which lasted for several hours.

This was what was to happen to him during sleep. Had he had the same power to project himself into the future he might have lost some of his optimism, realizing that while scientific and technological achievements proceeded apace in many directions, human nature remained the same, and that the conflict between the two was the fundamental issue of the twentieth century.

No one can say what he would have thought. It is all a matter of the purest speculation. All that we can ever know is that in spite of all he was one of the greatest Englishmen of all time, and that much of what we do know is due to his son, Henry Provost Babbage, who wished to be worthy of him, and who worked on parts of the analytical engine and gave them to the Science Museum in London, likewise to the British Museum the many volumes of his father's correspondence. It is in these and in his other inventions and writings that the fruits of Charles Babbage's genius lie. But they give no explanation of why, or how, his brain was as it was. This remains, with a number of other things, perhaps to our comfort, among the imponderables.

Appendix A

*

LADY LOVELACE compared the two engines, and then discussed the contemporaneous confusion of symbols. It is fascinating to see how she anticipated, or originated, much of the phraseology and ideas which are in current use today. Describing how the analytical engine might act upon other things as well as number, she said:

'Supposing, for instance, that the fundamental relations of pitched sounds in the science of harmony and of musical composition were susceptible of such expression and adaptations, the engine might compose elaborate and scientific pieces of music of any degree of complexity or extent.'

The analytical engine was to the difference engine as analysis was to arithmetic. The difference engine could do nothing but add, the other three processes of arithmetic being reduced to a series of additions. The method of differences was a method of additions. The analytical engine could add, subtract, multiply or divide, directly and without the aid of the other three. The difference engine could merely tabulate and was incapable of developing. The analytical engine could tabulate or develop. No finite line of demarcation limited the powers of the analytical engine. It afforded complete control over the executive manipulation of algebraical and numerical symbols.

Mathematics was not merely a vast collection of abstract and immutable truths, of intrinsic beauty, symmetry and logical completeness: it possessed a deeper interest. It was the language 'through which alone we can adequately express the great facts of the natural world.' Those who thought of mathematical truth 'as the instrument through which the weak mind of man can most effectually read his Creator's works will regard with special interest all that can tend to facilitate the translation of its principles into explicit practical forms.'

What made the analytical engine the executive right hand of abstract algebra was the principle which Jacquard devised for regulating, by means of punched cards, the most complicated patterns in the fabrication of brocaded stuffs. It was in this that the difference in the two engines lay. It could be said most aptly that the analytical engine wove algebraical patterns just as the Jacquard loom wove flowers and leaves. The difference engine was arithmetical, but the bounds of arithmetic were outstepped the moment the idea of applying the cards had occurred, and the analytical engine did not occupy common ground with mere calculating machines. It held a position wholly its own. The difference engine was exclusively synthetical, the analytical engine equally capable of analysis or synthesis.

She explained at some length the differences between the two engines, because she said much vagueness and inaccuracy existed in the minds of many people. The idea for the difference engine had nothing to do with the analytical engine. The latter did not grow out of the former. She emphasized that the difference engine had been long suspended when the analytical engine was first thought of, and she put up a spirited defence of Charles Babbage, hoping 'that for the honour of our country's reputation in the future pages of history these causes will not lead to the completion of the undertaking by some *other* nation or government. This could not but be matter of just regret.'

NOTE B

In this note Lady Lovelace alluded to the store which contained an unlimited number of columns of discs as described by M. Menabrea, her own description being 'a pile of rather large draughtsmen heaped perpendicularly one above another ... each having digits from 0 to 9 inscribed on its *edge* at equal intervals. . . .'

NOTE C

Here she explained that the applications of the cards, as in weaving, was not found sufficiently powerful, so the method of *backing* them was devised. This was a means of reducing the necessary number of cards.

NOTE D

Highly abstruse details on variables for data, working variables and variables for results formed the subject of this note.

NOTE E

This was the trigonometrical note, which had given her so much trouble, and was far too complicated for the non-mathematical reader to follow.

In it Lady Lovelace remarked that many people imagined that because the results were given in numerical notation, 'the *nature of its processes* must consequently be *arithmetical* and *numerical* rather than *algebraical* and *analytical*. This is an error. The engine can arrange and combine its numerical quantities exactly as if they were *letters* or any other general symbols'.

NOTE F

Lady Lovelace again referred to the backing system, giving mathematical examples of the reduction of the number of cards.

She described how problems which the human brain found difficult or impossible to solve, owing to the length and tediousness of the calculation involved, could be worked out by the machine, and she mentioned the problem of the Three Bodies. In the solution, 'out of about 295 coefficients of lunar perturbations given by M. Clausen . . . as the result of the calculations by Burg, of two by Damoiseau, and of one by Burckhardt, 14 coefficients differ in the nature of their algebraic sign; and out of the remainder there are only 101 (or about one-third) that agree precisely both in signs and amount'.

NOTE G

In this, the final note (H having been abandoned), Lady Lovelace took pains to discount exaggerated ideas and, at the same time, urging the reader not to underrate the powers of the analytical engine, which 'has no pretensions whatever to *originate* anything. It can do whatever *we know how to order it* to perform. It can *follow* analysis; but it has no power of *anticipating* any analytical relations or truths. Its province is to assist us in making *available* what we are already acquainted with'.

Abstruse mathematical calculations then followed. She remarked that the methods in Arbogast's *Calcul des Derivations* and the whole of Hindenburg's *Combinatorial Analysis* were peculiarly fitted for the notation and the processes of the engine.

Appendix B

*

CHARLES BABBAGE, who had more than one publisher, was on excellent terms with John Murray for many years, as is shown by about a dozen short letters which have been preserved, and which Sir John Murray very kindly allowed me to consult, in spite of the difficulties of receiving research students during the restoration of the historic house at Albemarle Street.

These letters range from 1837 to 1864, but they do not, unfortunately, throw any new light on Babbage's unpublished memoir of Lady Lovelace. It would seem that Murray either destroyed Babbage's letters or returned them to be destroyed.

Those in existence, however, confirm the date when Longmans Green, following Babbage's disagreement with Murray, published *Passages from the Life of a Philosopher*. On 21st June 1864 Babbage wrote: 'Messrs. Clowes are only waiting for the return of the title from you to print it off and in two days the whole will be ready.'

There is one other comment of interest. In view of his extreme sensitiveness he wrote, surprisingly enough, on 27th January 1848, to say that if Murray could suggest any corrections to one of his pamphlets he would be grateful for them, adding: 'I am not thin-skinned in such points.'

Notes

*

PROLOGUE

THE MAN

Alan M. Turing, F.R.S. *Mind*, October 1950.

D. R. Hartree, B.B.C. talk on Giant Calculating Machines, 1947.

B. V. Bowden, *Faster than Thought*, 1953.

$x^2 + x + 41$, the most famous prime generator discovered by Leonhard Euler, eighteenth-century Swiss mathematician, pupil of John Bernouilli.

Viscount Hailsham, 'Role of Higher Education in the Modern State, with special reference to Physics', 15th January 1962, reported in *Nature*, 10th March 1962.

Sir Charles Snow, *The Two Cultures and the Scientific Revolution*, 1959.

'It being sufficient . . .' *The Ninth Bridgewater Treatise*, 1838.

PART ONE

I THE SILVER LADY

C.B. to Statistical Society, Add. MSS. 37,199 ff. 429/30. The date and place of C.B.'s birth are given in *A List of the Babbage Family of Totnes, Devonshire*, compiled from Church Registers, Baptismal and Marriage Records, Various Deeds and Documents, by Henry P. Babbage, 31st December 1881. Also, note by H. P. Babbage, Add. MSS. 37,199, f. 551.

Benjamin Babbage and Praed's Bank. Private communication from Richard H. Babbage.

Benjamin Babbage haunted by spectres. Add. MSS. 37,196, ff. 5/17.

2 'MY DEAR CHARLES'

Totnes Grammar School. *The History of King Edward VI Grammar School, Totnes*, by Thomas H. Kelly, M.A. Totnes 1947.

F. W. Marryat on C.B. and himself as boys. *Captain Marryat*, by Oliver Warner, Constable, 1953.

3 THE DOT-AGE OF THE UNIVERSITY

Transfer from Trinity College, Cambridge, to Peterhouse. MSS. Buxton 16/17, f. 76.

C.B.'s allowance, from his account book. Private communication from Richard H. Babbage.

John Frederick William Herschel (1792–1871), only son of Sir William Herschel, discoverer of Uranus and private astronomer to George III. Educated at Eton and St. John's College, Cambridge. Senior Wrangler and 1st Smith's Prizeman, 1813. Distinguished chemist and astronomer. Profoundly interested in poetry, translating from Schiller and the Iliad. Knighted 1831, made a baronet 1833, buried in Westminster Abbey.

Edward Bromhead, son of Sir Gonville Bromhead, head of an ancient Nottinghamshire family, the latter's maternal ancestor, Edmund de Gonville, being joint founder in the fourteenth century of Gonville and Caius College, Cambridge.

C.B. to Higman. MSS. Buxton 16/17, f. 126.

C.B. to John William Whittaker, 26th November 1815. The Library, St. John's College, Cambridge, U.28.

4 GEORGIANA

Georgiana Whitmore's family and ancestors: information communicated by Gordon S. Babbage and Richard H. Babbage. See also Burke's *Landed Gentry*.

C.B. to Mrs. H. d'Arcy Stewart, 22nd September 1819. Add. MSS. 37,182.

Mrs. Stewart to C.B., 4th December 1819. Add. MSS. 37,182, f. 182.

Ibid., 6th January 1820. Add. MSS. 37,182, f. 197.

C.B. to Mrs. Stewart, April 1821. Add. MSS. 37,182, f. 327.

Ibid., May 1821. Add. MSS. 37,182, ff. 344/5.

Mrs. Stewart to C.B., 2nd December 1821. Add. MSS. 37,182, f. 392.

Edward Bromhead to C.B., 29th December 1819. Add. MSS. 37, 182, f. 184.

Ibid., 20th August 1822. Add MSS. 37,182, f. 431.

Captain F. W. Marryat to C.B., 8th February 1820. Add. MSS. 37,182, f. 217.

5 'SIR ALPHABET FUNCTION'

John Herschel to C.B., 27th July 1819. Add. MSS. 37,182, f. 123.

Edward Bromhead to C.B., 3rd July 1819. Add. MSS. 37,182, ff. 125/6.

Ibid., 27th October 1819. Add. MSS. 37,182, ff. 175/6.

'Sir Alphabet Function.' Unpublished text furnished by Richard H. Babbage.

Inebriated barrister to C.B., 4th August 1823 Add. MSS. 37,183.

Clergyman to C.B., 1st June 1827. Add. MSS. 37,184, f. 51.

A letter to Sir Humphry Davy, President of the Royal Society, on the Application of Machinery. London, 1822.

The Royal Society, incorporated by Royal Charter, 1662, probably the foremost scientific society in the world; encouragement is given to scientific investigation by awards of medals (Copley, Davy, Darwin and others) and the equipping of scientific expeditions.

Peter Mark Roget (1779–1860), physician, member of original senate, London University. Wrote *Thesaurus of English Words and Phrases* (1852).

Sir John Leslie (1776–1832), Professor of Mathematics and later of Natural Philosophy, Edinburgh University. Invented a differential thermometer, a hygrometer, a photometer and other instruments. Translated Buffon's *Birds*.

William Whewell, D.D. (1794–1866), fellow and tutor of Trinity College, Cambridge. Later became Master of Trinity and Vice-Chancellor of University. Published numerous works on scientific and philosophical subjects and translated from Goethe and others.

John Pond (1767–1836), Astronomer Royal and translator of Laplace.

Charles Hutton, LL.D. (1737–1823), F.R.S., Professor of Mathematics at Woolwich Arsenal.

Sir Joseph Banks (1744–1820), botanist. Accompanied Cook's voyage round the world, 1768–71, and gave name to Botany Bay. Elected President of the Royal Society in 1778 and held office for forty-one years.

Davies Gilbert (1767–1839), scientist, M.P. and topographer. President of Royal Society, 1827.

Jean Baptiste Biot (1774–1862), physicist and astronomer. Professor of Physics, Collège de France.

Silvestre François Lacroix (1765–1843), mathematician, author of famous works on the calculus.

Pierre Simon, Marquis de Laplace, (1749–1827), mathematician and astronomer. Most famous work, *Mécanique Céleste*.

6 THE PHILOSOPHERS OF LAPUTA

Sir Humphry Davy (1778–1827), distinguished chemist, most famous discovery being safety lamp. Created baronet 1818. Succeeded Sir Joseph Banks as President of the Royal Society, 1820.

C.B.'s remarks on difficulty of constructing difference engine, MSS. Buxton 16 and 17, f. 250.

7 NO TREASURY MINUTE

C.B. on language of signs, 'On a Method of Expressing by Signs the Action of Machinery', *Philosophical Transactions of the Royal Society*, 1826.

William Thomas Brande (1788–1866), chemist, F.R.S., and Davy's successor at the Royal Institution.

Sir Mark Isambard Brunel (1769–1859), engineer, knighted in 1851, his most celebrated undertaking being the Thames Tunnel (1825–43). His only son, Isambard Kingdom Brunel (1806–1859), was also a famous engineer, his works including Hungerford suspension bridge over the Thames at Charing Cross (1841–5), and all the tunnels, bridges and viaducts on the Great Western line. He designed the *Great Western*, first steamship built to cross the Atlantic, and the *Great Eastern*, largest vessel ever built at that time (1853–58).

Simeon-Denis Poisson (1781–1840), French geometer, professor and member of the Institute. Created peer of France in 1837. Wrote *Traité de Mécanique*.

Jean Baptist Joseph, Baron de Fourier (1760–1830), French mathematician, accompanied Napoleon to Egypt. Created Baron 1808. Author of *Theorée Analytique de la Chaleur*.

William Pearson (1767–1847), astronomer, F.R.S. and hon. LL.D.

Francis Baily (1774–1844), astronomer. Helped to found Royal Astronomical Society, and to improve *Nautical Almanac*. Published numerous papers in Royal Astronomical Society's *Memoirs*.

Thomas Frederick Colby (1784–1852), soldier, rising to rank of major-general and becoming director of the ordnance survey.

Henry Thomas Colebrooke (1765–1837), pioneer of Sanskrit scholarship.

Olinthus Gregory (1774–1841), teacher of, and writer on, mathematics.

Henry Kater (1777–1835), soldier and physicist, engaged in great trigonometrical survey in India and later worked at Military College, Sandhurst.

William Hyde Wollaston (1766–1828), M.D., fellow of Caius College, Cambridge. Distinguished two new metals, palladium and rhodium, in the ore of platinum. Made many contributions to optics. Elected second secretary of Royal Society, 1806.

Thomas Young (1773–1829), M.D. and physicist, becoming in 1801 Professor of Natural Philosophy at Royal Institution. Secretary of Royal Society.

8 'THE THING IS A HUMBUG'

C.B. on death of his father, wife and two children, 16th January 1871. Add. MSS. 37,199, f. 530.

Professor Airy's view of the difference engine. *The Diaries of William Charles Macready*. Ed. William Toynbee. Vol. I, Chapman & Hall, 1912.

C.B. and his family at Boughton, Worcester, and Georgiana's death, *The Memoirs and Correspondence of Major-General Henry P. Babbage*, 1910. Benjamin Babbage's Last Will and Testament.

Georgiana's last child, Alexander, lived for a very short time.

PART TWO

10 THE IRON DUKE IN SUPPORT

C.B.'s views on the Duke of Wellington as a military genius, *Exposition of 1851*.

Captain, later General, Sir Edward Sabine, F.R.S. (1788–1883), physicist. Accompanied Ross and Parry as astronomer in 1818–20. Noted for his work on terrestrial magnetism.

Edward Adolphus Seymour, eleventh Duke of Somerset (1775–1855), F.R.S. 1797. Published mathematical treatises.

Henry Goulburn (1784–1856), statesman. Chancellor under Wellington. Home Secretary under Peel, 1834–5. Chancellor 1841–6. Friend and executor of Peel.

Anthony Ashley Cooper, Lord Ashley, afterwards seventh Earl of Shaftesbury (1801–1885), philanthropist. Commissioner of the India Board of Control, 1828, under Wellington, and a Lord of the Admiralty under Peel 1834, active in every kind of good work, including ragged schools, factory workers, reform of lunacy laws.

John Rennie (1761–1821), engineer, built Southwark and Waterloo bridges over the Thames, in addition to many others. His sons, George (1791–1866), and John (1794–1874) knighted in 1831 on completion of London Bridge, carried on an immense business.

Sir John Franklin (1786–1847), Arctic explorer. Appointed to command expedition for discovery of North-West passage 1845, which he was the first to discover, later perishing in the *Erebus* and *Terror* disaster.

C.B.'s interview with Lord Brougham. Add. MSS. 37,199, f. 265.

Lord Brougham and Vaux (1778–1868), barrister and politician. Defended Queen Caroline 1820. Of Liberal views, served under aristocratic Whigs. Accepted peerage and Chancellorship 1830.

11 THE UNHAPPY ART OF MAKING ENEMIES

John Herschel to C.B., 17th November 1826. MS. Buxton 12.

Edward Ryan to C.B., 20th November 1826. Ibid.

Ibid., 24th November 1826. Ibid.

John Herschel to C.B., 25th November 1826. Ibid.

George Airy's election to Lucasian Professorship, 1826. *Autobiography of Sir George Biddell Airy, K.C.B.* Ed. Wilfrid Airy. Cambridge University Press, 1896.

C.B. to John Herschel, 20th May, 1821. Unpublished and undelivered letter furnished by Richard H. Babbage.

Nevil Maskelyne, D.D. (1732–1811). Educated Westminster and Trinity College, Cambridge. F.R.S. 1758, Astronomer-Royal, 1765, holding office for forty-six years.

C.B. accuses some members of Royal Astronomical Society of conspiracy against him, *Memoir of Augustus De Morgan*, by Sophia E. De Morgan, 1882.

Augustus De Morgan (1806–1871). Fourth wrangler at Trinity College, Cambridge, 1827. First Professor of Mathematics in University College, London. Secretary, Royal Astronomical Society, 1831–8 and 1848–54. Prolific writer on mathematical subjects. Father of William De Morgan, the novelist.

James South (1785–1867), astronomer. Elected President, Royal Astronomical Society, 1829. Knighted 1830.

George Dolland (1774–1852), noted instrument-maker.

Troughton & Simms, a noted firm of instrument-makers, now Cooke, Troughton & Simms.

12 CLEMENT DOWNS TOOLS

C.B. on Joseph Clement, 9th November 1869. Add. MSS. 37,199 f. 499.

J. Clement to C.B., 26th March 1833. P.R.O. T/134288. Clement became threatening. Writing on 22nd July 1833 he said that he had asked the Treasury whether they intended to 'exonerate' C.B. from payment of his account, but he does not exonerate him, and warns him that if any part of the machine is destroyed by fire he will not hold himself responsible. Add. MSS. 37,188, f. 14.

Sir John William Lubbock, 1803–65. Third baronet. Astronomer and mathematician. Educated Eton and Trinity College, Cambridge. F.R.S. 1829. Treasurer and Vice-President Royal Society, 1830–5 and 1838–47. First Vice-Chairman, London University, 1837–42.

13 BOTTOM OF THE POLL

C.B. to Alexander Forbes, Kingston, Jamaica. Add. MSS. 37,187, f. 4.

John Cam Hobhouse and Finsbury Election, MS. Buxton 12.

14 'TO BE MYSELF ONCE MORE'

Henry Babbage describes childhood days. *Memoirs and Correspondence of Major-General Henry P. Babbage*, 1910.

Sir David Brewster (1781–1868), natural philosopher. Elected F.R.S. and Copley Medallist, 1815, Rumford Medallist 1818 and subsequently Royal Medallist for discoveries connected with polarization of light. Invented kaleidoscope, 1816.

Dr. Dionysius Lardner (1793–1850). Appointed Professor of Natural Philosophy and Astronomy, University College, London, 1828. Published numerous works, including *Lardner's Cyclopaedia*.

Sir John Robison (1778–1843). Inventor. One of the founders of Scottish Society of Arts.

Rev. William Vernon Harcourt (1789–1871), general secretary, first meeting, British Association, York, 1831. Educated Christ Church, Oxford, Canon of York, conducted chemical experiments with Davy and Wollaston. Elected F.R.S. 1824. President, British Association, 1839.

Lambert Adolphe Jacques Quételet (1796–1874), Belgian statistician and astronomer. Showed uses to be made of theory of probabilities as applied to the 'average' man.

15 DESIGN FOR A 'BRAIN'

Joseph Marie Jacquard (1752–1834). Invented his famous loom 1801–8. Received small pension from Napoleon. Silk weavers so violently opposed his machine that on one occasion he narrowly escaped with his life.

Buxton on the analytical engine. MSS. Buxton 16 and 17.

C.B. to Chancellor of Exchequer, 29th January 1836. MSS. Buxton 16 and 17, f. 598.

17 INTERVIEW WITH PEEL

C.B. to Sir R. Peel. MSS. Buxton 16 and 17, ff. 610 and 612.

Sir George Airy on the Difference Engine. *Autobiography of Sir George Biddell Airy, K.C.B.*, ed. Wilfrid Airy. Cambridge University Press. 1896.

C.B.'s interview with Sir R. Peel. MSS. Buxton 16 and 17, ff. 616/642.

Peel's subsequent offer of baronetcy. Richard H. Babbage, private communication to author.

Peel's exoneration of C.B. in House of Commons. *History of the Royal Society*, by C. R. Weld. 1848.

PART THREE

18 FOREIGN MATHEMATICIAN: ENGLISH COUNTESS

Party at Dorset Street. *Memoir of Augustus De Morgan*, by Sophia E. De Morgan, 1882.

Attitude to Computing Machine, B. V. Bowden, *Faster than Thought*.

Albany Fonblanque on Countess of Lovelace. Biographical sketch of Lady Lovelace, from *The Examiner* reprinted in *The Life and Labours of Albany Fonblanque*, by his nephew, Edward Barrington de Fonblanque, Bentley, 1874.

A.A.L. to C.B., 18th January 1836. Add. MSS. 37,189, f. 281.

Earl of Lovelace to C.B., 4th February 1836. Add. MSS. 37,189, f. 319.

A.A.L. to C.B., 30th March 1838. Add. MSS. 37,190.

C.B. to A.A.L., 16th March 1839. Lovelace Papers.

Ibid., 29th November 1839. Ibid.

A.A.L. to C.B., 5th January 1841. Add. MSS. 37,191, ff. 532/3.

A.A.L. to C.B., 12th January 1841. Add. MSS. 37,191, ff. 543/4.

Ibid., 22nd February 1841. Add. MSS. 37,191, ff. 566/8.

Ibid., 11th August 1842. Add. MSS. 37,192, f. 126.

19 FAIRY FOR EVER

C.B.'s attitude to his sons, *Memoirs and Correspondence of Major-General H. P. Babbage*. Wm. Clowes, 1910.

C.B. to A.A.L., 30th June 1843. Lovelace Papers.

A.A.L. to C.B., N.D. 1843. Add. MSS. 37,192, ff. 360/1.

Ibid., 2nd July 1843. Add. MSS. 37,192, ff. 335/6.

C.B. to A.A.L., 2nd July 1843. Lovelace Papers.

A.A.L. to C.B., 2nd July 1843. Add. MSS. 37,192, ff. 337/8.

Ibid., 5th July 1843. Add. MSS. 37,192, ff. 350/3.

20 'AN UNCOMMONLY FINE BABY'

A.A.L. to C.B. about Prince Albert. Add. MSS.

Ibid., 10th July 1843. Add. MSS. 37,192, ff. 362/3.

Ibid., 19th July 1843. Add. MSS. 37,192, ff. 379/80.

Ibid., N.D. July 1843. Add. MSS. 37,192, f. 382.

Ibid., 26th July 1843. Add. MSS. 37,192, f. 390.

Ibid., 27th July 1843. Add. MSS. 37,192, ff. 393/4.

Ibid., 28th July 1843. Add. MSS. 37,192, ff. 399/401.

Ibid., 29th July 1843. Add. MSS. 37,192, ff. 401/3.

Ibid., 30th July 1843. Add. MSS. 37,192, ff. 407/9.

Ibid., 1st August 1843. Add. MSS. 37,192, ff. 414/5.

21 'MY DEAR AND MUCH ADMIRED INTERPRETRESS'

Prince Camille de Polignac to Lady Anne Blunt. Lovelace Papers.

C.B. to A.A.L., 5th August 1843. Lovelace Papers.

Sir Charles Wheatstone (1802–1875), F.R.S. 1836. Suggested stereoscope and spectrum analysis. Contributed to production and improvement of electric telegraph instruments, and made many improvements to submarine telegraphy, among other things.

A.A.L. to C.B., 11th August 1843. Add. MSS. 37,192, ff. 422/7.

C.B. to A.A.L., 9th September 1843. Lovelace Papers.

A.A.L. to C.B., undated. City of Nottingham Public Library.

C.B. to A.A.L., 12th September 1843. Lovelace Papers.

22 THE BOOK

Professor A. De Morgan to Lady Noel Byron, 1844. *The life and letters of Anne Isabella, Lady Byron.* Ethel Colburn Mayne, 1929.

A.A.L. to C.B., October 1844. Add. MSS. 37,193, f. 132 and 134.

Ibid., 22nd August 1845. Add. MSS. 37,193, ff. 228/9.

Ibid., 18th June 1846. Add. MSS. 37,193, ff. 387/8.

Charles Dickens to C.B., 26th February 1848. Add. MSS. 37,194, ff. 130/1.

A.A.L. to C.B., 30th September 1848. Add. MSS. 37,194, ff. 154/6.

Ibid., 18th October 1848. Add. MSS. 37,194, ff. 196/8.

Ibid., 2nd November 1848. Add. MSS. 37,194, ff. 203/6.

Ibid., 7th November 1848. Add. MSS. 37,194, f. 207.

Ibid., 12th November 1848. Add. MSS. 37,194, f. 214.

C.B. to A.A.L., 20th November 1848. Lovelace Papers.

Ibid., 29th November 1848. Lovelace Papers.

A.A.L. to C.B., 19th December 1848. Add. MSS. 37,194, ff. 232/3.

Ibid., 8th February 1849. Add. MSS. 37,194, ff. 250/1.

Ibid., 11th February 1849. Add. MSS. 37,194, f. 252.

A.A.L.'s admiration for Dickens, *The Life of Charles Dickens*, by John Forster, 1876.

A.A.L. to C.B., 20th September 1849. Add. MSS. 37,194, ff. 309/10.

Ibid., 28th September 1849. Add. MSS. 37,194, ff. 311/13.

W. M. Thackeray to C.B. 28th June 1850. Add. MSS. 37,194, f. 407.

C.B. to A.A.L., 22nd September 1850. Lovelace Papers.

23 THE CORONET, SLIGHTLY TARNISHED

A.A.L. to C.B., 1st November 1850. Add. MSS. 37,194, ff. 430/1.

C.B. to A.A.L., 13th May 1851. Lovelace Papers.

Ibid., undated. Lovelace Papers.

A.A.L. to C.B., 6th July 1843. Add. MSS. 37,192, ff. 355/6
and 13th July 1843. Add. MSS. 37,192, ff. 370/1

Ibid., 2nd September 1845. Add. MSS. 37,193, ff. 232/3.

A.A.L.'s racing losses, Mary, Countess of Lovelace, Epilogue, *The life and letters of Anne Isabella, Lady Byron*. Ethel Colburn Mayne, 1929.

A.A.L. to C.B., 12th August 1852. Lovelace Papers.

Ibid., Two notes in same envelope as above. Lovelace Papers.

Lady Noel Byron to a friend. *The life and letters of Anne Isabella, Lady Byron*, Ethel Colburn Mayne, 1929.

Reopening of Byron Vault. *Byron and Where He is Buried*, by Thomas Gerrard Barber. Henry Morley, Hucknall. 3rd Impression 1945.

C.B. to Wharton and Ford, 19th December 1852. Lovelace Papers.

Lady Noel Byron's paper on Mary Wilson. Lovelace Papers.

Lady Noel Byron to Rev. F. W. Robertson, 5th February 1853. Lovelace Papers.

Ibid., 13th February 1853. Lovelace Papers.

Rev. F. W. Robertson to Lady Noel Byron, 22nd March 1853. Lovelace Papers.

Ibid., 9th April 1853. Lovelace Papers.

C.B.'s Last Will and Testament.

PART FOUR

24 A BORE WITH EXTRAORDINARY TALENTS

Rev. Richard Sheepshanks, M.A. A letter to the Board of Visitors of the Greenwich Royal Observatory in reply to the Calumnies of Mr. Babbage at their meeting in June 1853 and in his book entitled *The Exposition of 1851*, G. Barclay, London, 1854.

C.B. and occulting light. *Memoirs and correspondence of Major-General H. P. Babbage*. Wm. Clowes. 1910.

25 HENRY AT DORSET STREET

C.B. to Miss Burdett-Coutts. Ibid.

Charles Dickens to C.B., 28th May 1844. Add. MSS. 37,193, ff. 71/2.

Charles Darwin to C.B., undated. Add. MSS. 37,197.

R. Hastings to C.B., Add. MSS. 37,197, ff. 11/12.

26 THE UNPHILOSOPHICAL PHILOSOPHER

Countess Harley-Teleki to C.B., 26th November 1863. Add. MSS. 37,199, f. 9.

Ibid., 10th December 1863. Add. MSS. 37,199, f. 13.

C.B. as a 'humorist manqué', Peter Dickinson of *Punch* in a private communication.

John Murray to C.B., 21st June 1863. Add. MSS. 37,198, f. 79.

Countess Harley-Teleki, 19th January 1864. Add. MSS. 37,199, f. 38.

C.B. to Emperor and Empress of the French. Add. MSS. 37,199, ff. 151/2.

Dr. John Davy to C.B., 6th September 1864. Add. MSS. 37,199, f. 115.

Prof. Lyon Playfair to C.B., 1st December 1864. Add. MSS. 37,199, ff. 160/1.

C.B. to Lyon Playfair, 12th December 1864. Add. MSS. 37,199, ff. 173/8.

Playfair to C.B., 20th February 1865. Add. MSS. 37,199.

27 'MY DEAR DUCHESS'

Catherine Sedgwick (1789–1867), author of *Redwood*, *The Linwoods* and other tales. Born at Stockbridge, Mass., U.S.A.

Henry W. Longfellow to C.B., 20th July, 1868. Add. MSS. 37,199, ff. 423/4.

Captain H. W. Howgate to C.B., May 1869. Add. MSS. 37,199, ff. 469/70.

Daniel Vaughan to C.B., 16th January 1871. Add. MSS. 37,199, f. 527.

C.B. to Countess Harley-Teleki, September 1865. Add. MSS. 37,199, f. 527.

Mrs. Ambrose Moore to C.B., 4th March 1869. Add. MSS. 37,199, f. 416.

C.B. to Countess of Rosse, 6th November 1867. Add. MSS. 37,199, f. 394.

C.B. to Lady Herschel, May 1871. Add. MSS. 37,199, f. 537.

C.B. to Duchess of Somerset. N.D. 1871. Add. MSS. 37,199, f. 518.

C.B.'s last illness and death. *Memoirs and Correspondence of Major-General H. P. Babbage*. Wm. Clowes. 1910.

The cause of death was renal inadequacy, secondary to cystitis.
Sir Victor Horsley, F.R.S., F.R.C.S. *Philosophical Transactions of the Royal Society of London*, 1908. Series B, Vol. 200, p. 119.

EPILOGUE

THE BRAIN

C.B.'s dreams in a letter to Sir Benjamin Brodie. Add. MSS. 37,196, ff. 9/17.

Bibliography

There are numerous works in which Charles Babbage is mentioned, but only those which have contributed important material to this biography appear below in chronological sequence.

Reflections on the Decline of Science in England, and on Some of its Causes. Charles Babbage. 1830.

On the Economy of Machinery and Manufactures. Charles Babbage. 1832.

The Ninth Bridgewater Treatise. Charles Babbage. 1837.

Sketch of the Analytical Engine invented by Charles Babbage Esq. L. F. Menabrea of Turin, Officer of the Military Engineers. Translated, with editorial notes, by the Countess of Lovelace. 1842.

A reply to Mr. Babbage's letter to The Times. Rev. Richard Sheepshanks. 1847.

History of the Royal Society. C. R. Weld. 1848.

The Exposition of 1851, or Views of the Industry, the Science and the Government of England, 2nd. Edn. 1851. Charles Babbage.

A letter to the Board of Visitors of the Greenwich Observatory. Rev. Richard Sheepshanks. 1854.

Passages from the Life of a Philosopher. Charles Babbage, Longmans. Green. 1864.

Personal Recollections of Mary Somerville. Martha Somerville. 1873.

Memoir of Augustus De Morgan, Sophia E. De Morgan. 1882.

Heroes of Science. T. C. Lewis. 1884.

Babbage's Calculating Engines. Henry P. Babbage. 1889.

Safe Studies. The Hon. Mr. & Mrs. Lionel Tollemache. 1895.

Three Score Years and Ten. Sophia Elizabeth De Morgan. Ed. by Mary A. De Morgan 1895.

Autobiography of Sir George Biddell Airy. Ed. by Wilfrid Airy. 1896.

Literary Eccentrics. John Fyvie. 1906.

Memoirs and Correspondence of Major-General Henry P. Babbage. Wm. Clowes. 1910.

The Diaries of William Charles Macready. Ed. William Toynbee. Vol. 1. Chapman & Hall. 1912.

Astarte. Ralph, Earl of Lovelace, 1921.

Lord Byron in his Letters. Ed. by V. H. Collins. Murray 1927.

The Life and Letters of Anne Isabella, Lady Byron, with an introduction and epilogue by Mary, Countess of Lovelace. Ethel Colburn Mayne. 2nd ed. Constable 1929.

The Authentic Arabian Horse. Baroness Wentworth. Allen & Unwin 1945.

Byron and Where He is Buried. Thomas Gerrard Barber. Hucknal. 3rd Impression. 1945.

The History of King Edward VI Grammar School, Totnes. Thomas H. Kelly, M.A. Totnes, 1947.

Faster than Thought. B. V. Bowden. Pitman 1953.

Byron. Leslie A. Marchand. Murray 1957.

Charles Babbage and His Calculating Engines. Edited and with an introduction by Philip and Emily Morrison. New York, Dover Publications. London, Constable. 1961.

Index

*

50 34